Counting: Ourselves and Our Families

A unit of study for grades K–1
from USED NUMBERS: REAL DATA IN THE CLASSROOM

Developed at Technical Education Research Centers and Lesley College

Susan Jo Russell and Antonia Stone

DALE SEYMOUR PUBLICATIONS

The *Used Numbers* materials were prepared with the support of National Science Foundation Grant No. MDR-8651649. Any opinions, findings, conclusions, or recommendations expressed in this publication are those of the authors and do not necessarily represent the views of the National Science Foundation. These materials shall be subject to a royalty-free, irrevocable, worldwide, nonexclusive license in the United States Government to reproduce, perform, translate, and otherwise use and to authorize others to use such materials for Government purposes.

Cover design and illustrations: Rachel Gage

Order number DS01038
ISBN 0-86651-517-8

DALE
SEYMOUR
PUBLICATIONS
P.O. BOX 10888
PALO ALTO, CA 94303

1 2 3 4 5 6 7 8 9 10-MA-95 94 93 92 91 90

USED NUMBERS STAFF

Co-principal investigators

Susan Jo Russell
Technical Education Research Centers (TERC)

Susan N. Friel
Lesley College

Curriculum development

Rebecca B. Corwin (TERC and Lesley College)
Tim Barclay (TERC)
Antonia Stone (Playing to Win)

Research and evaluation

Janice R. Mokros (TERC)
Alana Parkes (TERC)
Debra Gustafson (TERC)
John Olive (University of Georgia)
Deborah Ruff (University of Georgia)
Heide Wiegel (University of Georgia)
Bonnie Brownstein (Institute for Schools of the Future)
Ellen Bialo (Institute for Schools of the Future)
Michele Arsenault (Institute for Schools of the Future)
Mary Fullmer (University of Chicago)

Design and production

Elisabeth Roberts (TERC)
John Abbe (TERC)
Edith Alvarenga (TERC)
LeAnn Davis (TERC)
Jessica Goldberg (TERC)
Laurie Aragon (COMAP)

Cooperating classrooms for this unit

Peggy Hampton
Clarke County Public Schools, Georgia

Ann Ulmer
Clarke County Public Schools, Georgia

Christina Irwin-Astrove
Eliot Pearson Children's School, Tufts University

Jane Jacquith
Cambridge Public Schools, Massachusetts

Marcie Osinsky
Cambridge Public Schools, Massachusetts

Lynn Stinson
Cambridge Public Schools, Massachusetts

Advisory board

Joan Akers, California State Department of Education
Bonnie Brownstein, Institute for Schools of the Future
James Landwehr, AT&T Bell Laboratories
Steven Leinwand, Connecticut State Department of
    Education
John Olive, University of Georgia
David Pillemer, Wellesley College
Andee Rubin, Bolt Beranek and Newman Laboratories
Cindy Stephens, D. C. Heath
Marion Walter, University of Oregon
Virginia Wooley, Boston Museum of Science

Thanks also to advice and comment from Marilyn Burns,
Solomon A. Garfunkel (COMAP), and Bob Willcutt.

CONTENTS

Teacher Notes

PREFACE

In an information-rich society such as ours, statistics are an increasingly important aspect of daily life. We are constantly bombarded with information about everything around us. This wealth of data can become confusing, or it can help us make choices about our actions.

Educators and mathematicians now stress the importance of incorporating data analysis and statistics into the elementary mathematics curriculum to prepare students for living and working in a world filled with information based on data. The *Curriculum and Evaluation Standards for School Mathematics*, published by the National Council of Teachers of Mathematics in 1989, highlights statistics as one of the key content strands for all grade levels.

Many teachers see the need to support students in becoming better problem solvers in mathematics. However, it is difficult to find problems that give students the kind of experiences they need, are manageable in the classroom, and lead to the learning of essential mathematics. The area of data analysis—collecting, organizing, graphing, and interpreting data—provides a feasible, engaging context in which elementary grade students can do real mathematics. Students of all ages are interested in real data about themselves and the world around them.

Teaching statistics: Pedagogical issues

We introduce students to good literature in their early years. We do not reserve great literature until they are older—on the contrary, we encourage them to read it or we read it to them. Similarly, we can give young students experience with real mathematical processes rather than save the good mathematics for later.

Through collecting and analyzing real data, students encounter the uncertainty and intrigue of real mathematics. Mathematicians do not sit at desks doing isolated problems. Instead, they discuss, debate, and argue—building theories and collecting data to support them, working cooperatively (and sometimes competitively) to refine and develop such theories further.

Mathematicians and scientists use information or data like snapshots to look at, describe, and better understand the world. They cope with the real-world "messiness" of the data they encounter, which often do not lead to a single, clear answer.

Because statistics is an application of real mathematics skills, it provides the opportunity to model real mathematical behaviors. As students engage in the study of statistics, they, like scientists and statisticians, participate in:

▼ cooperative learning

▼ theory building

▼ discussing and defining terms and procedures

▼ working with messy data

▼ dealing with uncertainty

We want elementary school students to have the opportunity to engage in such real mathematical behavior, discussing, describing, challenging each other, and building theories about real-world phenomena based on their work.

Data analysis in the mathematics curriculum

Exploring data involves students directly in many aspects of mathematics. Data are collected through counting and measuring; they are sorted and classified; they are represented through graphs, pictures, tables, and charts. In summarizing and comparing data, students calculate, estimate, and choose appropriate units. In the primary grades, work with data is closely tied to the number relationships and measuring processes that students are learning. In the upper elementary grades, students encounter some of the approaches used in statistics for describing data and making inferences. Throughout the data analysis process, students make decisions about how to count and measure, what degree of accuracy is appropriate, and how much information is enough; they continually make connections between the numbers and what those numbers represent.

Instead of doing mathematics as an isolated set of skills unrelated to the world of reality, students can understand statistics as the vibrant study of the world in which they live, where numbers can tell them many different stories about aspects of their own lives. The computation they do is for a purpose, and the analysis they do helps them to understand how mathematics can function as a significant tool in describing, comparing, predicting, and making decisions. ■

TEACHING DATA ANALYSIS

The nature of data analysis

In data analysis, students use numbers to describe, compare, predict, and make decisions. When they analyze data, they search for patterns and attempt to understand what those patterns tell them about the phenomena the data represent.

A data analysis investigation generally includes recognizable phases:

▼ considering the problem

▼ collecting and recording data

▼ representing the data

▼ describing and interpreting the data

▼ developing hypotheses and theories based on the data

These phases often occur in a cycle: the development of a theory based on the data often leads to a new question, which may begin the data analysis cycle all over again.

Elementary students can collect, represent, and interpret real data. Although their work differs in many ways from that of adult statisticians, their processes are very similar. Elementary school students can both analyze data and use those data to describe and make decisions about real situations.

Because real data are the basis for investigations in data analysis, there are no predetermined "answers." For example, if your class collects data on the ages of the students' siblings, the students understand that their job is more than simply coming up with an answer that you knew all along. Not only do you *not* know the answer in advance, but, without seeing the data, you may not even know what the most interesting questions are going to be!

While this situation encourages students to do their own mathematical thinking, it can also feel risky for you. Many teachers welcome a little uncertainty in their mathematics classes, when it prods their students to be more independent thinkers. To support you, the authors provide sample experiences from teachers who have used the activities described here so that you can be prepared for the kinds of issues that are likely to arise. You will soon build your own repertoire of experiences with data analysis activities and will be able to anticipate likely questions, confusions, and opportunities.

The importance of discussion in mathematics

A central activity in data analysis is dialogue and discussion. While it is easy for you and your students to become engaged and enthusiastic in collecting data and making graphs, a significant amount of time should also be devoted to reflection about the meaning of the data.

Since students are not used to talking much during their mathematics work, it is important to support active decisionmaking by the students from the very beginning of the investigation. Students' participation in framing the initial question, choosing the methods of investigation, and deciding on ways to organize their data is essential. Once the data are collected and organized, the students must grapple with interpreting the results. If you have the outcome of a discussion or the "teaching points" you want to make too clearly in mind, you may guide students' observations too quickly into predetermined channels. When student ideas are ignored, misinterpreted, or rejected, they soon understand that their job is to second-guess the "answer" you had in mind.

On the other hand, if students find that *anything* they say is accepted in the same way, if every contribution is "a good idea" and no idea is ever challenged, they can lose motivation to participate. Ask students to reflect on, clarify, and extend their ideas and to listen to and ask questions of each other. Discussions in mathematics should encourage students to interpret numbers, make conjectures, develop theories, consider opposing views, and support their ideas with reasons.

Sensitive issues in data analysis

Students of all ages are interested in data about themselves and the issues they care about. Topics that matter enough to students to make them compelling topics for study often have very personal aspects. Investigations about families, heights, or students' chores, for example, can all bring up sensitive issues. After trying many topics in many classrooms, we have concluded that the potential sensitivity of a topic is not a reason to avoid it; on the contrary, these are the very topics that most engage student interest. All teachers deal with difficult or sensitive issues in their classroom, and the skills demanded of a teacher in handling issues that arise during data analysis activities are no different. Keep in mind that students may

sometimes want their data to be anonymous. Focusing on the patterns and shape of the class data, rather than on individual pieces of data, is particularly helpful, especially for upper elementary students.

Small-group work

Many of the investigations involve students working in teams. At first, keep small-group sessions short and focused. For students not used to working in small groups, assign specific tasks that encourage the participation of all the group members. For kindergarten and first grade students, working in pairs is a good beginning.

Materials

Students need materials to represent their data during their investigations. These range from Unifix cubes to pencil and paper to computer software. What is most important is that students are able to construct multiple views of the data quickly and easily and that they do not become bogged down in drawing and coloring elaborate graphs (which are appropriate only at the very end of an investigation when students are ready to "publish" their findings).

Any material that can be moved easily and rearranged quickly offers possibilities for looking at data. For example, students might write or draw their data on *index cards* (or any paper rectangles); then these can be arranged and rearranged. *Unifix cubes* (or other interconnecting cubes) are

another good material for making representations throughout the grades. We have found that *stick-on notes* (such as Post-it notes), with each note representing one piece of data, are an excellent material for making rough drafts of graphs. They can be moved around easily and adhere to tables, desks, paper, or the chalkboard. *Pencil and unlined paper* should always be available for tallies, line plots, and other quick sketch graphs.

Calculators

Calculators should be available, if possible, throughout the activities. Their use is specifically suggested in some of the investigations. It is no secret to students that calculators are readily available in the world and that adults use them often. But many students do not know how to use a calculator accurately, do not check their results for reasonableness, and do not make sensible choices about when to use a calculator. Only through using calculators with appropriate guidance in the context of real problems can they gain these skills.

Computers

Computers are a key tool in data analysis in the world outside of school. Graphing software, for example, enables scientists and statisticians to display large sets of data quickly and to construct multiple views of the data easily. Some software for the elementary grades allows this flexibility as well. A finished graph made by the computer may, for some students, be an appropriate illustration for a final report of their findings. But keep in mind that students also make interesting and creative graphs by hand that would not be possible with the software available to them. Other computer software, including software for sorting and classifying and data base software, is particularly useful for some data analysis investigations. Where the use of a software tool would particularly enhance a data analysis investigation, recommendations for incorporating its use are made in the text and noted at the beginning of the session.

Home-school connections

Many opportunities arise in data analysis investigations for communicating with parents about the work going on in the classroom and for including them as participants in your data investigations. When you begin this unit, you may want to send a note home to parents explaining that students will be studying data analysis in their mathematics class and that, from time to time, parents can be of assistance in helping students collect data from home. Parents or other family members often provide an available comparison group. Studies of age, family size, height, and so forth can be extended to include parents. If students are studying their own families, they may be interested in collecting comparison data about their parents' families. Including parents and other significant family members as participants in your data analysis investigations can stimulate their interest and enthusiasm for

the work students are doing in school and, at the same time, help students see that the mathematics they do in school is connected to their life outside of school.

Interdisciplinary connections

Many teachers find ways to connect the data analysis experiences students have in mathematics to other areas of the curriculum. Data analysis is, after all, a tool for investigating phenomena of all kinds. The same approaches that students use in this unit can be called on for an investigation in science or social studies. Making these connections explicit and helping students transfer what they have learned here to new areas will give them an appreciation of the usefulness of mathematics throughout the curriculum. ■

COUNTING: OURSELVES AND OUR FAMILIES
UNIT OVERVIEW

Counting: Ourselves and Our Families is a unit of study in which young students use counting to collect data about themselves and their environment. Suitable for students in kindergarten and first grade, it provides experiences through which students deepen their understanding of numbers and the many ways numbers can describe aspects of the world.

The unit offers a series of questions that connect closely to young students' own knowledge and experience: When is your birthday? How old are you? How many of you are there in this class? Altogether, how many eyes do all the people in this room have? As students investigate these questions, they collect, record, and discuss real-world data. This unit prepares students for further work in collecting and analyzing real data, such as that provided by the next five units of the Used Numbers series, designed for grades 2–6.

In Counting: Ourselves and Our Families, students:

▼ count themselves, other groups of students, objects in their classroom, parts of their body, and other immediate aspects of their environment

▼ record and represent these counts using a variety of concrete materials, pictures, and graphs

▼ describe their results and make comparisons using their results

How to use this unit

Like the other Used Numbers units, *Counting: Ourselves and Our Families* is organized into investigations. Each investigation consists of a series of related problems built around a topic that is developmentally and mathematically appropriate for kindergarten and first grade students. At this level, an investigation will take from 3 to 6 class sessions of about 45 minutes each, and is generally completed in one or two weeks. A schedule of 2–3 sessions per week works best to maintain continuity while allowing enough time for reflection and consolidation between sessions.

The investigations in this unit are closely related to key issues in children's learning about number: one-to-one and many-to-one correspondence, associating the counting numbers with objects and quantities, comparing quantities, and finding ways to represent numbers and data. There are five investigations:

▼ *Birthdays*

▼ *How many of us?*

▼ *Nobody here, nobody there*

▼ *Counting noses*

▼ *Our ages*

The activities are sequenced so that students move gradually from more straightforward to more complex investigations. Most teachers who have used this unit have spread these investigations through the school year. For example, one kindergarten teacher presented *Birthdays* during the third week in September, then did *How many of us?* in October, *Nobody here, nobody there* in November, *Counting noses* in January, and *Our ages* in March. The first three investigations are particularly appropriate for the first few months of the year, while *Counting noses* and *Our ages*, which deal with numbers in the 30s, 40s, 50s, and possibly beyond, might be put off until later.

The unit brings together work in counting, sequencing, comparing, computation, graphing, and data collection in a problem-solving context. Because this unit was designed for both kindergarten and first grade students, the investigations, along with the suggested extensions, have considerable range in terms of the concepts and number relationships students encounter. All of the investigations have been used successfully with 4- to 7-year-old students. However, you will need to vary the emphases and the timing of each investigation according to the knowledge and experience of your students. In general, the earlier investigations are tied to earlier concepts in understanding number, such as

one-to-one correspondence, while later investigations explore larger numbers and involve more complex representations.

Whether you teach kindergarten or first grade, we do suggest that you try most of the activities with your students, even those that at first appear too easy or too difficult. Many teachers found that there was hidden complexity for students in activities that looked "easy"; others were surprised by the interest students showed for exploring larger numbers in activities that had appeared to be beyond their reach.

Planning the investigations

In this book, you will find four types of information for each investigation:

Investigation overview. This section includes (1) a summary of the student activity, (2) materials you will need for the investigation and any special arrangements you may need to make, and (3) a list of the important mathematical ideas you will be emphasizing. Plan to look carefully at this overview a day or two before launching the investigation.

Session activities. For each session, you will find step-by-step suggestions that outline the students' explorations and the teacher's role. Although suggestions for questions and instructions are given, you will of course modify what you say to reflect your own style and the needs of your students. In all cases, the teacher's words are

intended to be guidelines, not word-for-word scripts. Plan to read through this section before each session to get the general flow of the activities in your mind.

Dialogue Boxes. The Dialogue Boxes illustrate the special role of discussion in these investigations and convey the nature of typical student-teacher interactions. Examples are drawn from the actual experiences of classes that have used these investigations. They call attention to issues that are likely to arise, typical student confusions and difficulties, and ways in which you can guide and support students in their mathematical thinking. Plan to read the relevant Dialogue Boxes before each session to help prepare for interactions with your students.

Teacher Notes. These sections provide important information you will need in presenting this unit. The Teacher Notes include discussions of how children develop their understanding of numbers and number relationships, examples of mathematical and nonmathematical issues that are likely to arise during the activities in this unit, and suggestions for supporting children who are just beginning to use mathematical tools such as counting, estimating, and graphing.

The Teacher Notes are listed in the contents because many are useful as references throughout the unit, not just where they first appear. For example, *On the verge of a big idea* (page 39) talks about the many different things K–1 students are discovering about number, and how the teacher can help. You might plan to read all the Teacher Notes for background information before starting the unit, then review them as needed when they come up in particular investigations.

Goals for students

The "Important mathematical ideas" listed in each investigation overview highlight the particular student goals for those sessions. Once a particular goal has been introduced, it continues to be developed through experiences in later parts of the unit. The major goals for *Counting: Ourselves and Our Families* are as follows:

Finding out information for yourself. The fundamental assumption underlying collecting and using real data is that we can investigate aspects of the world and discover information for ourselves without relying on outside authority to tell us the "facts." Young children can develop their own resources and strategies for uncovering information, solving problems, and making decisions.

Counting provides information about a group of things. Students are gradually making the transition from thinking of counting as a string of words to using counting as a tool for describing aspects of their world. Just as "red" describes one characteristic of a bowl of apples, "five" describes a different characteristic of those apples. This information is often useful in making decisions about situations in the real world.

Developing counting strategies. Even when young children understand the correspondence between a count and an object, counting a number of objects is still a challenging task. We all have strategies for making sure we have counted accurately—such as moving each object as we count it to an "already counted" pile, or by keeping track of the spatial arrangement of the objects, so that we know where we started counting and where we should end. These are strategies that students need to invent, try out for themselves, and talk about many times.

Matching one-to-one. When two sets of objects are matched, one object in one set with exactly one object in the other set, each set has the same number of objects. This one-to-one correspondence means that if there are 26 students, and each student has exactly one nose, there are 26 noses.

Matching two-to-one. If there are exactly two objects in one set for each object in another set, there is a two-to-one correspondence. For 26 students, each of whom has two arms, there will be twice the number of arms as students. This early exploration of many-to-one counts is the foundation upon which a great deal of mathematics is built, including multiplication, division, and ratios.

Representing what has been counted. Students experiment with different ways of organizing and representing the things they have counted. Their methods of organizing data may not be like adults' methods, but they need to try different ways, talk about them, and sometimes change them, rather than simply copying adult methods. They need to construct many different kinds of representations, sometimes using concrete materials, sometimes drawing pictures, and sometimes building graphs.

Describing data. A critical skill in data analysis at any level is describing the information that is conveyed by a pictorial representation of the data. At this level, students are most interested in their individual pieces of data ("My birthday is on November 14"), but they also begin to notice other aspects of the data ("No one has a birthday in March," "October is the king of the birthdays") and to show interest and surprise about certain features of the data ("My birthday and Fernando's are exactly 10 days apart," "I can't believe there are two children born on the same day and they are not twins").

Comparing quantities. As students compare the counts of various objects, they develop their sense of the relative sizes of numbers. Which numbers are close together? Which numbers are farther away from each other? How close to 20 is 17? Is 23 closer?

Counting above 20. The names of the numbers occur in a regular way in each decade, starting with the twenties. Some students will already know this pattern; others will be working hard to learn it. Students who are right in the middle of learning this pattern will often count, "25,

26, 27, 28, 29 . . . what's the next one? [*someone prompts, "30"*] . . . oh, yeah, 30, 31, 32, 33 . . . " At this point, the child knows the interior pattern and is learning the names of the decades—20, 30, 40, and so forth.

Visualizing quantities. As students learn the names of the numbers, they simultaneously begin to visualize "how big" those numbers are. They need to do this in many situations, with concrete objects and materials of all kinds, so that they are continually developing their sense of the size of quantities in comparison to other quantities.

Comparing several categories of data. Some data collection questions beginning with the words "How many . . ." can be answered with a single number. But questions that begin "How many more . . ." or "How many less . . ." require categorizing the data so that the number of items at each value can be compared. For example, students compare the number of 5-year-olds, 6-year-olds, and 7-year-olds in their class.

Displaying information about several categories. Students are introduced to simple representations that allow them to compare categories, including bar graphs and tallies.

Finding and comparing numbers on a hundred board. Through working with the hundred board and locating numbers on it, students explore the structure, order, and patterns of the number system: All the 30s are in a row, all the "zero numbers" go down one side of the board, and so forth. As students gain experience, they will become familiar with patterns that will help them locate numbers on the board more quickly. These patterns will later connect to ideas about place value and the structure of our number system.

Displaying information to show both values and categories. Students encounter a more complex kind of representation toward the end of this unit, for example, when they display the ages of themselves, their sisters, and their brothers. This graph shows two dimensions of the students' data—age (e.g., 5 or 20) and category (e.g., brother or sister)—at the same time. ■

BIRTHDAYS

INVESTIGATION OVERVIEW

What happens

In order to plan a series of monthly birthday celebrations, students collect and organize information about their birthdays. After a general discussion about what a birthday is, students decide on ways to figure out how many of them have birthdays in each month. They make cards showing their birth dates and display these cards, grouped by months. The second session is spent ordering the cards by months and then by dates within the month and describing the information that the completed chart conveys. In the final session, the class makes a plan, based on their chart, for special treats for those with birthdays in each month.

The activities take three class sessions of about 45 minutes each.

What to plan ahead of time

▼ Before Session 1, make sure all students know when their birthdays are. They may need to find out this information at home. In all kindergarten and first grade classes that used the trial version of this unit, some students did not know their birth dates. Although you have this information on record, students will be more involved in the investigation if they find out this information for themselves—and in doing so, they will also involve their families in their data collection. You may want to prepare a sheet for students to take home with a place to write down their birth dates. More than one incorrect birthday in school records has been discovered through this activity!

▼ Prepare a set of "birthday cards" on large (5-by-8-inch) index cards or on half-sheets of 8-1/2-by-11-inch paper (Session 1). You will need one card for each student, with the month of birth at the top in large print and blanks for the student to fill in the exact birth date and his or her name.

Using your school records, you can estimate the number of cards you will need for each month, but include a couple of extra cards for each month, as well as a couple of cards for any month in which none of your students has a birthday. It is important that the month names be printed in large letters.

▼ Plan how you will display the birthday cards grouped by months (Sessions 1 and 2). They can be tacked onto a bulletin board, clipped onto a clothes-line, or taped onto the chalkboard. Whatever method you use needs to be flexible so that students can reorder the cards during Session 2.

▼ Obtain a variety of calendars for students to use as resources (optional, Sessions 1–3).

Important mathematical ideas

Finding out information for yourself. The fundamental assumption underlying collecting and using real data is that we can investigate aspects of the world and discover information for ourselves without relying only on outside authority to tell us the "facts." As adults we learn that even if those facts are given, we can still evaluate information for ourselves. Young children, too, can develop their own resources and strategies for uncovering information, solving problems, and making decisions.

Comparing sizes of groups. As students investigate how many of them were born in each month, they compare groups and describe the differences among these groups by using the language of comparison: *more, less, about the same, a lot more, only a few,* and so forth.

Organizing a display. Students discuss how to display the birthday cards so that they can tell which birthday is next. Organizing data is a critical skill, one that these students are only just beginning to develop. They need to consider and decide for themselves how best to organize their display.

Describing data. Another critical skill in data analysis is describing the information conveyed by a pictorial representation of the data. At this level, students are most interested in their individual pieces of data ("My birthday is on November 14"), but they also begin to notice other aspects of the data ("No one has a birthday in March," "October is the king of the birthdays") and to show interest and surprise about certain features of the data ("My birthday and Fernando's are exactly 10 days apart," "I can't believe there are two children born on the same day and they are not twins").

Noticing the cyclical nature of the sequence of months. The months are an interesting sequence. No matter where you start the sequence you can, as one child said, "keep going and going." The sequence of counting numbers also keeps going and going, but no number is repeated. The months, in contrast, cycle back to the beginning, and the 12-month sequence is repeated again and again.

Becoming familiar with numerical features of the calendar. As students make their birthday chart, they consider how many months there are in a year, how many days there are in a month, and the order of the dates within each month. ■

SESSION 1 ACTIVITIES

Introducing the problem: What is a birthday, anyway?

Start the discussion by setting out the purpose of this investigation—to plan special birthday treats for each student's birthday. However, see the Teacher Note, *Birthday customs* (page 16).

We are going to be collecting information about your birthdays so we can make our plans. But before we do that, who has an idea about what a birthday is?

Students' responses are likely to include ideas such as these:

"It's when you get older . . . When you have a birthday cake . . . When you invite kids over and you get to play outside . . . It's when you are born . . . Every time you have a birthday you get older and older and older and older."

At first students are likely to talk only about what they *do* on their birthdays. To get beyond this, you might comment:

So a lot of you have a cake on your birthday, but why is that day special? What is a birthday?

The main point of this discussion, as for others you will conduct during this unit, is to encourage many students to share their views and to listen to what other students

say. Not all students will end up with the same idea about what a birthday is, but everyone will have heard ideas that are not the same as their own, thereby extending their understanding. In discussions like these, you might want to list students' basic ideas on the board, perhaps in a short form (e.g., birthday cake, party, the day you were born, older and older). Even though your students will not be able to read all the words, lists like this can be used for language experience work: choral reading, having children read their own contributions, finding specific words, and so forth.

Recording the data: When is your birthday?

How many of you know what month your birthday is in?

Ask a few students to say when their birthdays are. Write the months on the board in the order they are mentioned.

Let's see—we have May, October, and July. Who has a birthday in a different month?

List as many months as the students can think of on the board or a large piece of chart paper. This is a good time for a discussion of how many months there are.

Do we have all the months here? Which ones are missing?

Students may suggest that you write the months with no class birthdays in a different

spot. Follow their suggestions for writing all the months. If students know that there are 12 months but cannot think of them all, leave blank spaces for the "mystery months" for now. See the Teacher Note, *Finding out for yourself* (page 16). If students do not know that there are 12 months, or if there are differing opinions about the total number, list on the board all the students' ideas about how many months there are and leave this as another "mystery" to be solved.

How could you find out what the missing months are? How could you find out for sure how many months there are?

Ask students to follow up on these ideas, either later in the day or as homework.

On a table or other large surface, set out the "birthday cards" you have prepared, with a stack of cards for each month. Don't be concerned about ordering the months at this point. Have students come up in pairs or threes and help each other select the appropriate month from the stacks of cards (of course, you can help, too, as needed). Students then fill in their birth dates and write their names on the cards, so each card looks something like this:

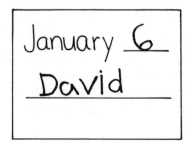

Organizing the data: How many in each month?

Now let's find out how many of you have birthdays in each month. We need to know how many are in October, and how many are in June, and how many are in each of the other months. How could we use your cards to find this out?

Spend enough time on this discussion so that many students have a chance to offer suggestions, even if some of their ideas are the same. See the Dialogue Box, *Anybody else with May?* (page 15), for excerpts from such a discussion in a first grade classroom.

Follow one of the student suggestions about how to organize the data. Often classes decide that all students with the same month should find each other and make a group. Without any direction about which group should go where, first graders are able to do this. Of course, there may be a bit of initial confusion, but students enjoy the involvement of the physical activity and are able to form their groups successfully.

Each group has to solve the problem of making sure everyone for their month is in their group. Some groups send out scouts to check other groups. Some students suggest that they all hold their cards over their heads so they can look around the classroom and check. Sometimes two groups will be formed for the same month, but students usually discover this and correct it by themselves.

Once students have found their groups, ask for some brief reports of what they can see by looking around the room ("There's 3 in our group," "I'm the only one for January," "That's the biggest group by the windows"). Encourage students to use language that describes comparison: *about the same, bigger/smaller than, more, less.*

If there is still time and interest, try one of the other student suggestions for finding out how many are in each group.

Have each group bring up their birthday cards and put them together so that everyone can see all the months. You might tack them on the bulletin board or clip them onto a clothesline, so that your display looks something like the one shown below.

At this point, do *not* put the months in order; just put them up however you happen to get them from the students. The class will be working on a *sequence* for the months in the next session.

Let students know that you will be talking about their birthday chart during the next session. If there are unresolved "mysteries" about the months (How many months are there? What are the missing months?), ask students to see if they can come up with an answer to one of these "mysteries" before the next session. They can work together or alone and they can use any resources they can find in the classroom or at home—except for asking an adult. This problem can be a homework challenge, or there may be times they can work on this during the school day.

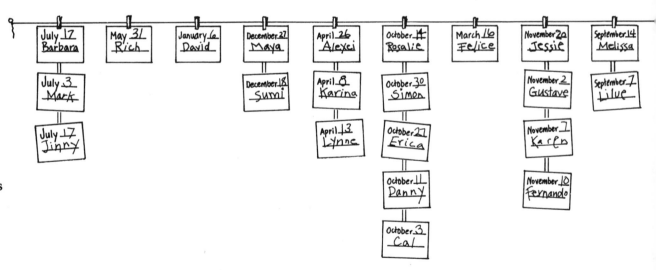

They can report on what they found out and how they did it during the next session.

☞ Don't be concerned if you have already made a different sort of birthday display in your classroom. Simply emphasize that the purpose of this one that the students are making is to plan birthday treats. For example, one teacher started this investigation in mid-October, even though the class had already made a birthday display at the beginning of September. The students were perfectly happy to make a new display, and in the course of this investigation, many students revisited and consolidated work they had done earlier.

Extensions

▼ Build towers of interconnecting cubes in different colors, one for each month. A small group of students might enjoy working on this project, using the chart of birthday cards as a reference.

▼ Have several different calendars around the room or in the book corner for browsing. Some might be calendars for the current year while others may be old calendars. What stays the same each year? What changes? ■

❝❞DIALOGUE BOX
Anybody else with May?

What are some ways we could tell how many people in our class have a birthday in each month? What could you do to find this out?

CAL: Count the months.

Count the months? How would you do that?

CAL: Like April, January, October [*counts on his fingers as he says each month*].

And what would that tell us?

LYNNE: How many months.

OK, how many months. So what if I wanted to know how many of you have a birthday in October? How could I find that out?

SUMI: We've got the cards. All we have to do is hold up our cards and count and we could just write them down on a piece of paper and we can see.

RICH: I would find out if anybody else has May.

How would you find out? What would you do?

RICH: I would just take my card with me and go see which ones are the same as mine and I'd count how many.

SIMON: I would walk around the room and touch everybody with the same as mine, and that would be how many for October.

So Rich would count the cards and Simon

would walk around and count the people. Is there another idea?

JANE: Yeah, all the April people could stand together, and then all the October people, and the same for each month, and then each month would know how many.

DANNY: We could take the cards and put them up.

How would you do that?

FERNANDO: Like in a line, all the ones for each month.

And how would that help us know how many in each month?

DANNY: Because you would just count down the line, 1, 2, 3, and that's all, so if that were like April, you'd know.

Interesting. Put all the people together is one way. Put the cards together is another. Jesse?

JESSE: I have a really good idea. Take the Unifix cubes and put it with different colors. Like all the reds for April and all blues for December and keep on going like that.

I'm not quite sure I get it. How would I put the cubes?

JESSE: Take red, and you go around, and for each kid with April you put a red.

ERICA: And then you count them up.

KAREN: You could make a tower for April.

JESSE: And a different color for May. Like that. ■

✎TEACHER NOTE
Birthday customs

Everybody enjoys having their own special day. The goal of this investigation is to plan a special day for each student in the class or for a small group of students in each month.

Your school may have a policy that precludes your having snacks or birthday parties in school. However, students have come up with many ideas for birthday "treats" that are not edible (see the Dialogue Box, *Ways to celebrate birthdays in school,* page 20); they can be very creative in planning a birthday celebration that is not a traditional party.

Also keep in mind as you begin this investigation that some cultural and religious groups de-emphasize individual birthdays. Some students may celebrate a special day that is not their birthday. Keep discussion open at the beginning of these activities so that students can talk about particular customs that their families follow. Make sure to encourage discussion of diverse views of birthdays.

When planning the monthly treats in Session 3, you may want to call these "special days" instead of "birthday celebrations" so that any students who do not celebrate birthdays can still feel part of the celebration. ■

✎TEACHER NOTE
Finding out for yourself

One of the key ideas behind this unit is the idea that you can find out information for yourself. Young students have a lot of authorities in their lives from whom they get a great deal of information and advice. However, even kindergarteners and first graders need to learn that they can find out information using their own resources. In the beginning, your students will probably believe that the only way to obtain factual information is to ask someone for it. You need to encourage them to develop other strategies as well—that is what collecting data is all about.

This means that you must be particularly alert in identifying questions to which the students can find their own answers. For example, when a student asks, "What month comes after February?" it is tempting simply to reply, "March." If, instead, you suggest that the two of you go over to the wall calendar, you will be empowering your student by adding to his or her resources.

It is certainly not possible, or desirable, to send students out to find their own answers for every question they have. Consider what happens with students' endless questions about how to spell particular words. On the one hand, you don't want to give them a spelling lesson or send them to the dictionary every time they ask how to spell something.

On the other hand, if someone is always willing to spell the word for them, students will develop no resources of their own. A better alternative is to develop approaches that encourage students to use everything they know about letter symbols and their sounds before they turn to adult authority. These might include accepting students' "invented spelling" in some situations, or establishing resources, such as the children's own files of words, that they can use directly.

Similarly, in mathematics, it is not always appropriate to say "figure it out yourself," nor is it always appropriate to simply give the answer. You can help your students expand their repertoire of strategies for tackling unfamiliar problems by providing a concrete material with which they can model the problem, by steering them to a useful resource in the classroom, by reminding them about another problem they solved, by suggesting collaboration with another student, or by encouraging them to collect their own data.

As one kindergarten teacher commented about her students' experiences in collecting data, "It's awakened in them an interest in finding out things about people and about each other. There's a whole kind of accessibility of finding out information—and then using that information in some way—that I haven't seen before." ■

SESSION 2 ACTIVITIES

Describing the data: What can we tell about our birthdays?

Ask students to take a look at the birthday chart you made at the end of the last session.

Suppose someone who didn't know us came along and saw this chart. What could that person find out from the chart?

Students are first likely to notice information about individuals ("They could see that my birthday is in June," "Lilue's birthday is on September 7"). They may also begin to generalize information about how many birthdays occur in different months, as in this exchange from one classroom:

JANE [*pointing*]: There's 3 at this one, 2 at that one.

RICH: January is less, it has only one.

MAYA: No, the less is zero, a lot of months have zero.

SIMON: Ms. Carlson, that's the biggest! October is the king of the classroom because there's more there than any other month.

Follow up with questions like these:

Whose birthday is in March? What is the date of her birthday? What four children have birthdays in the same month?

As children become familiar with the chart, you could ask them to pose their own questions that they think can be answered by looking at the chart.

Organizing the data: Whose birthday comes next?

Pose a new question to the group:

If we wanted to know whose birthday is coming next in the school year, and then what's the next one and the next one, what could we do to our display so that we could tell?

This question leads naturally to a discussion about what order to put the months in, how many months there are, and which months are missing. During this discussion, ask any students who have information on the "mysteries" (the number of months, the names of the missing months) to talk about what they found out and how they found it out.

During this discussion, encourage different points of view about how to order the months. As adults, we immediately assume that a list of months should start with January and end with December. When we give students this pre-ordered list, they do not have the chance to think for themselves about the problem of putting the months in order. If students are reluctant to contribute ideas—perhaps because they assume you want them to tell you the usual calendar order—ask explicitly for different possibilities:

Karima and Melissa want to start with January, like the calendar does. Can anyone think of a different way we could start?

Some classes decide to start with January; some with September (the beginning of school); some with the current month. Sometimes students suggest alphabetical order. Even though you know this sequence is incorrect as a way to show which month follows which, give students the chance to resolve the issue themselves through discussion, rather than explaining yourself why this won't work.

If students have strong opinions about two different plans for ordering the months, you may want to try them both; students can then look at them, compare them, and decide which one to use for this investigation.

In this discussion, the idea that the sequence of months is cyclical is likely to come up. In one class, for example, the students eventually decided to begin the chart with the current month (October), with each month following in order, and to move October to the "end of the line" when it was over, and so forth, so that the current month would always be first and they would know whose birthdays were in that month. As one student observed, "You can't stop the months. The months just keep going, going, going, going."

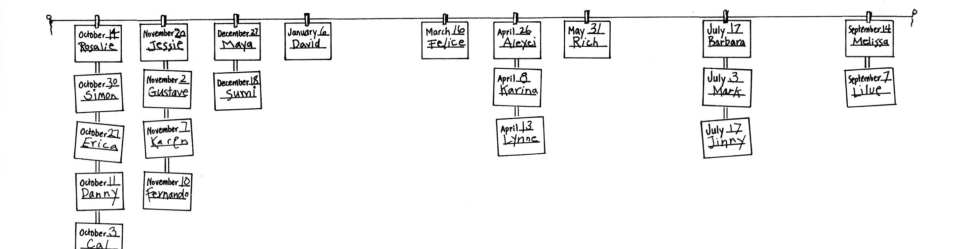

Rearrange the birthday chart according to what the students decide. Discuss how many months there are and, if any are missing, what those are and how to indicate them on the chart.

If students have not yet brought up the problem of ordering students' birth dates within each month, prompt them with a question.

Now that we have the months in order, can I tell which birthday is the next one, and which one comes after that?

Give students lots of time to share their ideas about what else to do with the birthday chart. See the Dialogue Box, *What comes next?* (page 19). As students reorder the chart, ask them to explain how they know the order of the numbers ("Why did you put 18 before 25?").

Once the chart is finished, ask students once again to describe what someone looking at their chart could find out.

☞ We suggest that you save this birthday chart along with all the other graphs, pictures, and charts that students will be making throughout the unit. They are often helpful in providing information or comparisons during subsequent investigations. ■

66 99 DIALOGUE BOX
What comes next?

Now that we have the months in order, can I tell which birthday is the next one, and which one comes after that?

STUDENTS [*variously*]: Yes . . . No . . . No . . . Yes . . .

How can you tell?

ERICA: October is the first month.

October is this month, so all five October birthdays come before the others? Because they're all in October? OK. Can you tell which one of the October people comes first?

DANNY: Yes.

How can you?

DANNY: You need to lay them in order.

What do you mean in order? I thought they were already in order by months.

[*Danny goes to the chart and puts the October cards in order by date.*]

Did you see that? He changed around our October people's cards. Danny, what do you mean they're in order?

DANNY: Because, see, which one comes first, the numbers keep on getting higher and higher.

SUMI: We could do that for all the months.

We could. What would we do for November?

[*Later*] . . .

Why did you do December that way? How can you be sure?

LYNNE: You know 18 comes before 27 because the teens always come before the twenties.

What do you notice now that we have the days in order?

JESSE: There's exactly 10 days between Fernando's birthday and mine.

How did you know that?

JESSE: Because his is on a 10 and mine is on a 20.

ROSALIE: There's a double in July.

CAL: I can't believe there are two children born on the same day and they are not twins! ∎

SESSION 3 ACTIVITIES

Using the data: Planning birthday treats

There are two questions to be discussed in this session: When will we celebrate everyone's birthdays? What "special treat" will we have for the celebration?

Much interesting discussion grows out of these two questions. Start by focusing on one of the months in which there are several birthdays. Ask the students how you could pick a special date for that month. Some classes decide to celebrate on each student's birthday; others decide to have one day each month that is the special day for all the students born in that month.

For various reasons, you may want to limit the "special day" to one a month. If the class (or you) decides on one day each month, how will that day be chosen? Should it be on the first birthday that comes up that month? The last? A day exactly in the middle of the month? How can you figure out where the exact middle of the month is? (This is a wonderful problem for pairs of students to work on, using a page from a calendar.)

Another part of the discussion will focus on what to do about students with summer birthdays and/or students with birthdays in months that have already passed for this school year. Probably students will bring up this issue themselves. If not, you can. This question has often provoked lively talk about what to do. Students' ideas have included suggestions such as these:

▼ "Put all the summer people into February because no one has a birthday in February."

▼ "January, March, and May only have one birthday, so some summer people could celebrate with them."

▼ "The summer people should get to choose which month they want."

After this decision is made, you may want to make a second chart with your students, showing the dates chosen for celebrations and the names of the students to be honored on each of those days.

Finally, students plan what the "special treats" will be. You will set the guidelines for this discussion, given whatever customs and policies you or your school have. One teacher set the following guidelines: The treats could not involve food and could not take away too much learning time.

After brainstorming a list of possible ideas, each birthday group can meet together to choose their treat. Then help the class list the treats for the special day in each month. For one group's ideas, see the Dialogue Box, *Ways to celebrate birthdays in school* (following). ∎

66 99 **DIALOGUE BOX**
Ways to celebrate birthdays in school

One group of first graders had the following ideas:

> extra play time
> bring little goodies
> no board writing
> play extra games
> the teacher plays with us outside
> the birthday kids are teachers
> have story time outside
> make masks
> read books for fun
> carve a jack-o-lantern
> make scary things
> go to the big playground
> take a walk and watch the leaves change
> fly kites

This class had also been talking about the characteristics of different months, so some of the ideas (kites, jack-o-lantern, autumn leaves) were connected to what they knew occurred in particular months. After each birthday group met to choose their treat, the class made a chart of their choices.

Celebrating Our Special Days	
October	carve a jack-o-lantern
November	have story time outside
December	go to the big playground
January	birthday kids get to be teachers
February	(no birthdays)
March	fly kites
April	walk to the river
May	extra playtime
June	(no birthdays)

HOW MANY OF US?

INVESTIGATION OVERVIEW

What happens

Students use several different ways to count and represent the number of people in their class: first a large class chart, then individual charts, self-portraits, and finally concrete materials.

The activities take three class sessions of about 45 minutes each.

What to plan ahead of time

▼ Prepare a large piece of squared chart paper with the title, *This is how many we are* (Session 1).

▼ Provide stick-on dots for the large class chart (optional, Session 1), or crayons or markers

▼ Provide squared paper with large squares (you can duplicate page 73) and

markers, crayons, or stick-on dots for students to make their own pictures of the number of people in the class (Session 1).

▼ Provide materials for students to make their self-portraits. These will vary according to the option you choose; see page 27 (Session 2).

▼ Provide materials for students to make their own concrete models of the number of people in their class (Session 3). These might include shells, buttons, paper clips, tiles, blocks, drawing paper, heavy paper on which to paste shells or buttons, crayons, scissors, and paste, glue, or tape. Offering a variety of materials is likely to spark children's imaginations about different ways to represent how many are in the class.

▼ Provide calculators for individual student exploration and for small group

work (optional, Sessions 1–3). See the Teacher Note, *Young children can use calculators* (page 41).

☛ Save the dot charts and self-portraits students make in these activities, as they will be useful for comparison in a later investigation, *Counting noses.*

Important mathematical ideas

Counting provides information about a group of things. Students are gradually making the transition from thinking of counting as a string of words to using counting as a tool for describing aspects of their world. Just as "red" describes one characteristic of a bowl of apples, "five" describes a different characteristic of those apples. This information is often useful in making decisions about situations in the real world. In order to use counting, young children must coordinate a complex set of ideas about numbers and what they represent, as discussed in the Teacher Note, *Critical ideas in understanding number* (page 25). Throughout these activities, students gain experience with counting and numbers that helps them consolidate these ideas.

Developing counting strategies. Even when young children understand the correspondence between a count and an object, counting a large number of objects is still a challenging task. We all have strategies for making sure we have counted accurately—such as moving each object as we count it to an "already counted" pile, or by keeping track of the spatial arrangement of the objects, so that we know where we started counting and where we should end. These are strategies that students need to invent, try out for themselves, and talk about many times.

Representing what has been counted. Students experiment with different ways of organizing and representing the number of people in their class. Their methods of organizing data may not be like adults' methods, but they need to try different ways, talk about them, and sometimes change them, rather than simply copying adult methods. ■

SESSION 1 ACTIVITIES

Introducing the problem: Why do we need to know how many of us there are?

As we get to know each other better, we're going to be collecting a lot of information about ourselves and our families. We can find out a lot of important information by counting. Today we're going to start by finding different ways of counting how many people are in this class.

Can you think of any reasons why we might need to know how many are in our class? Think for a minute about different times when you or I or other people might need to know how many of us there are.

Pause and give students time to think of ideas. Encourage them to clarify and extend their ideas, or ask other students to help explain a difficult idea. See the Dialogue Box, *Why do we need to know?* (page 24).

Collecting data: Counting in different ways

Now we are going to try some different ways of counting how many of us there are. Who can think of something we can try? How can we make sure that we count everyone?

Students may well suggest that they can just count everyone in the room, or that you

count the names on the class list. Follow up with questions like these:

Suppose we try to count everyone in the room—how can we make sure we count everyone and that we don't count anyone twice? Who has a way that would help us keep track of which people we counted?

Follow one or two of the students' suggestions. They may include the following:

▼ Count each student as he or she stands up, one at a time.

▼ Start with everyone standing up, and count each student as he or she sits down.

▼ Sit in a circle and count everyone in order.

▼ Each student takes a block or other object to the teacher's desk; then the class counts the objects.

▼ Each student writes his or her name or makes a tally mark on the chalkboard; then the class counts these marks.

Ask students to explain why each method works. Encourage them to discuss why they get the same total each time—or, if they don't, why they don't. Be careful that the total number of students—say, 23—is not used as a "right answer" to verify students' counting strategies. *You* know that their counting should come out to 23 each time, but some students in your class may be just discovering this idea.

Recording data: Making a class dot chart

Post, within student reach, the large squared chart paper you have prepared with the title *This is how many we are*.

I want to make a picture to show how many of you there are, so anyone could look at it and tell how many people are in this class without having to find you all and count you. We're going to show on this paper exactly how many are in this class by having each of you put up a stick-on dot [or, make a crayon dot] in one of the squares.

Students take turns coming up to the chart and putting a dot in one square. Together, keep an oral count as each person adds to the chart. Or, you might have students come up to the chart in small groups and recount the total after each group has made their marks. For example, one teacher asked five students at a time to come up and put their dots on the chart; after each group, the class counted how many dots were on the chart altogether.

This is how many we are.

Throughout these activities, give students leeway to construct the representations in

their own way. For example, in this particular activity, students may scatter their dots around on the chart rather than proceeding from left to right and from the top row to the next. Some students may want to have the dots placed one after the other, with no squares skipped, but let this suggestion come from the students. If appropriate, once the chart is finished, follow student suggestions for reorganizing it so that they can count the dots more easily.

During counting, watch to see which students coordinate their counting with the objects they are counting and which ones simply say a string of numbers without making sure that they correspond to the objects. One teacher made a game out of connecting each counting number to a dot by pointing to the dots in an erratic rhythm— sometimes slower, sometimes faster, some- times stopping unexpectedly—to help focus on the number-object connection.

If, as is likely, one or more students are absent, be sure that the issue of counting the absent student(s) is discussed. If no student brings up this issue during the activity, you can ask, after they have finished their count:

So is 23 exactly how many students are in this class?

Such a question will probably prompt some students to remember that someone is absent. Discuss how many students there would be if the absent student(s) were

present. If no student is absent now, this issue will probably arise naturally in one of the later sessions when someone is gone.

Recording data: Individual dot charts

Give each child a piece of squared paper (page 73) and either a sheet of stick-on dots or crayons or markers.

Each student makes his or her own dot chart to show the number of students in the class. Students can sit in small groups of three or four during this activity, so they can help each other make sure they have the same number of dots as students in the class. Some students may use counting to make their chart accurate. Others will copy the pattern from the large class chart. As students finish, ask them to explain to you how they know that their chart shows the number of students in the class.

☛ If you are doing this session near the beginning of the year, the dot activity is an excellent one to help you assess your students' understanding and facility with numbers and with counting. See the Teacher Note, *Watching students count* (page 25).

Extension

If you have a regular morning meeting time or a time when you take attendance, have students decide on different ways of counting how many students are in class each day. ■

❝❞DIALOGUE BOX
Why do we need to know?

Can you think of some times when people need to know how many of us there are?

DAVID: Maybe they need it for a certain reason.

For a certain reason? Can anyone think of one?

JINNY: They need to know how many people to get that many books.

For books?

JINNY: Like reading books.

MAYA: Yeah, like when everybody in my group got *A Kiss for Little Bear*.

OK. Who can think of another time?

BARBARA: In case we're taking a field trip and Alexei got left behind and we don't know she's missing.

Did anyone ever use counting when they were on a trip?

MARK: Last year Ms. Santiago took us on the bus and we each had a number, and there were 23 kids, and each time we'd get off the bus or on the bus we'd count off.

KAREN: And my mom does it all the time.

What does she do, Karen?

KAREN: Like when we go to the zoo, she goes 1, 2, 3, 4, 5, 6 all the time to make sure we're all there.

KYLE: When there was a fire some people could be inside.

So what would you do?

KYLE: You could count everyone as they came out the door, and then you'd know.

There are lots of times when I need to know how many of you there are. Can you think of any?

ROSALIE: For sending the attendance to the office.

RICH: When you got pencils for everyone.

PAUL: The day we made that snack with the apples and peanut butter, you had to know how many apples.

I remember when Erica's mother brought cupcakes for her birthday.

ERICA: I told her how many.

And when Simon's dad brought the cookies.

SIMON: He didn't know how many. He just got a big old box of cookies in three packs and that was all.

That's a real interesting one. He didn't know exactly how many, so how did he know that he had enough cookies?

SIMON: Well, cause a big bag would be enough.

OK. Any other ideas how Simon's dad was sure he had enough even though he didn't need the exact number?

CAL: Well, he'd know it wasn't 100 or anything.

Oh! So he knew the number was less than 100. What else do you think he knew?

LYNNE: He'd know it was less than 50.

FERNANDO: Yeah, because a class wouldn't be 50. And he'd know it was more than, like, 10 or 11.

GUSTAVE: But maybe he'd need 100 for everyone to have two.

So sometimes we need the exact number, like when Mark's class went on the trip last year, and sometimes we can just know *about* how many, like when Simon's father brought the cookies and he estimated about what number would be reasonable.

☞ In this discussion, students have offered a variety of reasons for counting the number of students in the class. The teacher is careful to give students the chance to extend their own or others' ideas and is on the alert for important mathematical ideas that come up in the discussion, such as when you need exact information and when an estimate will suffice. ■

Students in the same kindergarten or first grade class can vary considerably in age and in their previous experience with numbers. While most students will have learned to count by rote, they are still exploring the ways in which those numbers give information about quantities of real things. Just as being able to say the alphabet does not indicate that a student can use written language, being able to say, "1, 2, 3, 4, 5, 6, 7, 8, 9, 10," does not necessarily indicate that a student knows how those numbers are related to each other or to quantities they might represent.

Many of the activities in this unit provide the opportunity for you to observe your students' work with numbers and to gain insight about their varied understandings of numbers, quantities, and numerical relationships. For example, in one kindergarten class that included 4-, 5-, and 6-year-olds, the teacher learned a great deal about her students as she watched them work with their dot charts and, later, with number charts. Some children counted accurately, while others did not coordinate the numbers they said with the objects they were counting. Some children had to recount each time one more object was added to a collection, while some knew that, if they had 5 objects, adding one more gave them a total of 6 objects. Some

students could read and write most of the numerals up to 20; others could recognize only a few of the numerals. As one child commented, when someone pointed out a 9, "I thought that was a *P*." A few were already exploring more abstract numerical relationships. Said one 6-year-old, looking at a number chart, "12 is really 3 plus 3 plus 3 plus 3."

The teacher in this classroom was fascinated by the wide range of ways in which her students were exploring numbers. You are likely to have a wide range in your classroom, even if your age range is not quite as large as hers. Watching your students carefully as they work will give you clues about which ideas are new to them and how you can ask questions tailored to each student's progress toward understanding numbers. ■

Throughout this unit, students use counting to describe situations in their world. Many of your students may still be grappling with very basic ideas about number. Consider this excerpt from a conversation between 6-year-old Joey and his teacher as they look together at a classroom hundred board. It shows the complexities underlying the ways in which young children encounter numbers.

When we counted this morning, do you remember how many kids were here today?

JOEY: 21.

Can you find 21 on the board?

JOEY [*pointing at each number with his finger*]: 1, 2, 3 . . . 21! That's it, a 2 and a 1. That's 21.

What other numbers can you find on here?

JOEY: This is me, I'm 7. And this is my older brother—he's 13—and my little sister is 2—that's right here.

How much older are you than your little sister?

JOEY: I don't know.

How many years older are you? Any way you could figure it out on here?

JOEY [*pausing*]: No.

What other numbers do you see on here?

JOEY: There's 33—that's Larry Bird's number, and 44 is Danny Ainge.

Forty-four is . . . ?

JOEY: Danny Ainge . . . on the Celtics.

Oh, his number on his shirt.

JOEY: Yeah.

So this is Larry, 33, and this is Danny, 44. Which is bigger?

JOEY: Larry's taller.

Oh, Larry's taller!

JOEY: My brother's room number is two-twelve. Is that on here?

Like most children in the primary grades, Joey has many numbers in his life—numbers that are used to count objects, numbers that measure quantities, and numbers that are labels and do not represent quantities. In these early years, it is important that the curriculum be geared to helping students sort out all the ways that numbers are used.

In particular, students are developing their understanding about these key ideas:

▼ The counting numbers can be used both to count objects and to describe the quantity of those objects. Some students may still be coordinating these two aspects of number—the *ordinal sequence* of the numbers with the *cardinal meaning* of those numbers.

We get to 5 by counting 1, 2, 3, 4, 5 in order. In this ordinal sequence, 4 comes after 3, and 5 comes after 4. Understanding this aspect of number is connected to the one-to-one correspondence between the numbers we say and the objects we are counting.

However, being able to count accurately—using this ordinal sequence—is not the same as knowing that, when we are finished counting, the final number in our counting sequence tells the quantity of the things we have counted. The last number we said in the counting sequence—for example, 5—tells us the quantity we have.

This understanding is closely tied to conservation of number: Whether that group of objects is stretched out, bunched together, separated into two piles, or hidden from view, it will still have 5 objects, as long as no objects are added or taken away.

▼ The names and symbols we use to describe quantity have patterns that correspond to the underlying structure of our number system. A young child who counts "twenty-eight, twenty-nine, twenty-ten" is actually making a sensible generalization about how these words describe quantities, just as the child who says "I runned away" has learned something about the regularities of our language. As students use the counting numbers in many different contexts, they discover more about the

patterns and relationships among these numbers.

▼ Numbers can be transformed through operations, such as combining two groups of objects or splitting up a quantity into parts. Operations such as these make numbers a powerful and predictive thinking tool in understanding all sorts of real situations. The discovery that it is possible to figure out how many cookies are left, without counting them, given the information of how many there were and how many have been eaten, is a landmark in the development of number concept.

Just as all children learn how to speak, all children eventually understand and use the multiple meanings of number they encounter in their daily lives—but students develop this understanding in different ways and at different rates. By providing your students with many kinds of counting activities in many different contexts, you give them experience with the ways in which numbers describe the world and help them begin to coordinate the many different meanings that the same number has. ■

SESSION 2 ACTIVITIES

Representing the data: Portraits of the class

Yesterday you made this large dot chart showing how many people are in our class. Today you're going to make another display to show how many of you there are—and it will show some other things about you, too.

In this session, each student makes a self-portrait. There are many different ways to accomplish this, and you may have your own favorite approach. Here are some of the ways teachers have carried out this activity:

Crayon self-portraits. Each student draws a self-portrait with crayons and paper.

Brown paper people. Using large rolls of brown paper (or butcher paper), trace and cut out each student's full body outline. Students then color in details of hair, eyes, features, and clothing. This approach requires ample time, some extra adult help, and enough space to display the results. Teachers have found that the small rolls of brown paper sold for wrapping packages curl up too much after they are cut; try to find a large school or art supply roll. If you pre-cut a large rectangle for each student and can get a couple of parent volunteers to help, the outlining of the students goes pretty quickly. Some students may need help cutting.

Index card display. Each student draws a self-portrait on a 5-by-8-inch index card. These cards can then be strung across the room, using clothesline and clothespins.

Silhouettes. One teacher drew and cut out a silhouette of each child's head. She darkened the classroom, pinned black paper to the bulletin board, and sat each child, in turn, on a chair in front of the paper, while another student held a flashlight on the seated child's profile. Each silhouette took about one minute to draw. Although the students did not create these silhouettes themselves, they were fascinated with the process and enjoyed identifying them once they were hung up in the room.

Photographs. Some teachers take photographs of each child and mount them on cardboard for permanent use. Such photos can be used for counting and sorting throughout this unit. You may want to have more than one set of these class photos.

Describing the data: What does it tell us?

After the self-portraits are completed and displayed, compare this display with the large dot display on chart paper that you made in Session 1.

If someone came into the classroom who didn't know anything about you, what could they find out from your dot chart? What could they find out from your self-portraits?

In this discussion, students will probably notice that the dot display provides, in a compact space, information about the number of people in the class that is relatively easy to count, but it does not give any information about individuals. The self-portraits may show a lot of information about individuals—hair color, whether they wear glasses, and details of their clothing, for example. ■

SESSION 3 ACTIVITIES

Representing data: Exploring pictures and patterns

On a table or shelf within reach of all students, assemble the materials for constructing their concrete models.

So far you have made dot charts and self-portraits to show how many people are in our class. Today I want you to choose other ways to show how many of you there are.

Point out to the students what materials are available and ask for ideas of what they could make to show how many students there are. Make sure each student has his or her small dot chart for reference.

Students can work together in small groups, but each one is to make his or her own representation of the class. Some may choose to make a chain of paper clips. One group made chains out of paper strips, with one link for each child in the class. Many students used their dot charts and laid shells, tiles, or buttons directly on the charts

to get the correct number of students. Then they pasted their shells or buttons on another piece of paper to make a permanent display. Students who used this one-to-one correspondence method often arranged the shells or buttons into patterns, once they had the correct number, and then glued them onto paper. Some children might draw a picture that shows the total number of students or has some symbol for each one.

While some students may want to write the numerals (from 1 to 23, say) to show how many are in the class, at this age level it's easy to get bogged down in trying to write all the numerals; in the process, students often lose track of the quantity they are dealing with. Therefore, discourage work with numerals at this point, at least until students have first made models or pictures. Instead, challenge them to show "how many" *without* using numbers,

As you move around the classroom, ask students about their methods. Ask them how they know their models or pictures show exactly the number of students in the class. See the Teacher Note, *How do you know it's exactly the number of students in the class?* (opposite page).

Encourage students to write a title for their model, such as *There are 23 of us.* You may want to have each child dictate a sentence to describe his or her model or picture. If possible, display all the student representations on a bulletin board and/or table.

Extension: Using hundred boards

Some students will enjoy making similar concrete models on hundred charts. You can reproduce one of the hundred charts on pages 67 or 69, or you may want to obtain the more permanent hundred charts made of plastic or laminated cardboard and available from school materials suppliers. Students can place buttons, shells, or other counters directly on the hundred board, just as some may have placed them on their dot charts in Session 3.

At this level, some students will just be starting to learn the sequence and names of the numerals. Through this work, they can begin associating the *names* of the numerals (which they know from counting) with the *written symbols*. Other students, who already recognize the symbols and are familiar with their order, may enjoy playing the following game on the hundred board:

Cover up all the numbers from 1 to the total number of students in the class (use tiles, interlocking cubes, or cardboard squares). One student points to one of the tiles, and other students try to guess what number is covered up, just from its placement on the board. They may use a variety of strategies—counting from the beginning, or counting from the beginning of the row. At first, you might leave some numbers uncovered to give students some clues; or, you might leave each number uncovered as it is guessed. ■

✎ TEACHER NOTE
How do you know it's exactly the number of students in the class?

It is obvious to us, as adults, that if we put a dot for each student on the chart, then there will be 23 dots if there are 23 students. However, this correspondence is not necessarily obvious to 5- and 6-year-olds. In these activities, students are developing very basic ideas about how a model—like a set of buttons—can "represent" another set of objects, such as the students themselves.

One pair of students carefully placed a button on each dot on their dot chart, then rearranged the buttons in a long line across the desk. They counted the buttons several times and were finally satisfied that there were 23 buttons:

What did you do with the buttons?

DANNY: We put a button for every dot, and we counted them and there are 23.

FELICE: See, 1, 2, 3 . . . [*she continues to count*] . . . 21, 22, 23!

And what do your buttons show about the kids in the class?

DANNY: There's one for every kid.

How do you know?

DANNY: Because these [*points to the dots*] are the kids in the class and we gave one button to every kid.

FELICE: And there's 23 kids and 23 dots and 23 buttons!

How did you figure that out?

FELICE: Because I counted the dots and there's 23 and we counted the kids before. At first I thought it was 22 dots, but then we counted a lot of times and it was 23.

Uh-huh. So you know because you counted? Is there any other way to know?

DANNY: Yeah, cause there's one dot for every kid and one button for every kid and so they're all the same.

Danny's understanding of the correspondence of dots, buttons, and students is somewhat different from Felice's. Felice "knows" there are 23 because she counts and she proves this by counting again. If she miscounts, she might believe that there are a different number, as she was at first willing to accept that there might be 22 buttons. During this experience, Danny has developed a stronger "proof." He thinks that there must be 23 buttons because there is a button for each student. He does not need to recount the buttons, once he knows that they are matched to the 23 dots.

The teacher was careful not to turn the investigation into a search for the "right answer," as happens in this exchange:

And what did you use to show all the students in the class?

STUDENT 1: Shells.

And did this show that there are 23 of us?

STUDENT 2: Yes.

How do you know?

STUDENT 2: Because we counted them, 1, 2, 3 . . . [*continues counting*] . . . 21, 22, 23, 24, 25 . . . no, that's too many . . .

Let's count again. Let's do it together, 1, 2, 3 [*continues counting with the students*] **. . . 21, 22, 23! So does this show there are 23 of us?**

STUDENT 1: Yes.

There is a subtle, but critical, difference between this conversation and the episode with Felice and Danny. In this second episode, the students may not be at all sure that the number of shells matches the number of students in the class. They know only that the count comes out to "23," when someone helps them count correctly, and that "23" is "supposed" to be the answer. They have no chance to find out for themselves that they have 23 in each set—students, dots, shells—and to forge their own understanding of this correspondence.

Danny and Felice, through the teacher's open-ended questions, had a chance to build their own understanding. The teacher did not push Felice to accept Danny's version. With many opportunities for counting, comparing, and working with other students, Felice will also develop further understanding of the ways in which numbers represent quantities. ∎

NOBODY HERE, NOBODY THERE

INVESTIGATION OVERVIEW

What happens

Students work in pairs to count and record the number of something in the room, such as coats or desks, that would provide a clue about how many students are in the class. After developing ways to estimate the number of students in their own class, they try out their strategies in another classroom. They visit the class when the students are not there, count a variety of objects, record their data, and decide what their estimate is for the size of that class. An optional cookie-baking activity is suggested so that students can provide a treat when they report on their "detective work" to the other class.

The activities take four class sessions of about 45 minutes each, not including making the cookies.

What to plan ahead of time

▼ Provide things to count with (cubes, beads, buttons, drinking straws) and a container (plastic bag or paper cup) for each pair of students (Sessions 1 and 3).

▼ Provide drawing paper, scissors, and glue, as well as a variety of objects for students to represent their data (Session 1).

▼ Arrange with another teacher a time when your class can visit his or her classroom while the students are not there. You will probably need 20–30 minutes in the empty classroom (Session 2 or 3).

▼ Decide whether you will make or buy cookies or another treat for the other class and, if you are going to do so, allow time for this between Sessions 3

and 4. If you do not have cooking facilities but can manage a "no-bake" cookie, you may want to try the recipe provided with this investigation (page 38). These were a favorite of one of the author's young students.

▼ Provide squared paper with small squares (you may duplicate page 71) or interlocking cubes for students to record their data (Session 3).

Important mathematical ideas

Collecting data through counting. Students continue to count as they record the number of a variety of objects in the classroom. Working in pairs, they develop strategies for keeping track of their count.

Finding ways to estimate the number of something. By counting objects related to people (coats, desks), students find ways to estimate the number of students in a class. Building on their work with one-to-one correspondence in the *How many of us?* investigation, they consider situations that are close to, but not exactly, one-to-one correspondences. Students begin to consider how close an estimate has to be to give them the information they need.

Comparing quantities. As students compare the counts of various objects, they continue to develop their sense of the relative sizes of numbers. Which numbers are close together? Which numbers are farther away from each other? How close to 20 is 17? Is 23 closer? Students use representations that allow them to compare one quantity with another. ■

SESSION 1 ACTIVITIES

Introducing the problem: Nobody here

Ask how someone might figure out the total number of students in your class if that person came into the room when nobody was there.

We've been finding ways to show how many of you there are in this class. Suppose you didn't know that there are 23 children in this class, and you looked into our room early in the morning before anyone was here. What clues would you see that would you help you find out how many people are in the class?

You might want to ground this conversation in a hypothetical situation in which such an estimate would be useful:

Suppose Jesse's dad wanted to send in cookies tomorrow and he dropped by to check on how many cookies he would need, but we were at lunch [on the playground, in the gym]. What could he count that might give him a number really close to the number of students in the class?

Students will probably immediately think of the representations and self-portraits they made recently. Encourage students to think of all the possibilities they can and pursue their ideas about which things would give good estimates and what problems might arise for people as they tried to count. Students can usually draw on their common

sense to come up with a range of feasible ideas. See the Dialogue Box, *Everyone has coats!* (page 33).

In this discussion, try to strike a balance between listing lots of possibilities and pursuing in more depth some of the students' suggestions. As students contribute their ideas, you can introduce the word "estimate" into the conversation naturally. See the Teacher Note, *On estimating* (page 35).

Collecting data: Counting in pairs

Students work in pairs to count and record the number of some object in the room that they think would give a good idea of how many people there are in the class. Ask each pair to choose one thing to count, so that a lot of different things are counted. It is also fine if some pairs count the same thing, so you can compare different counts. See the Teacher Note, *Is it 21 or 22?* (page 39).

Provide some kind of counting material and some kind of container (a plastic bag, a paper cup) for each pair. One class used bundles of drinking straws; others have used beads, buttons, or interconnecting cubes. Students use the counters to record their count.

Working in pairs will be hard work for some students. For suggestions on helping students develop cooperative strategies, see the Teacher Note, *Working in pairs* (page 36).

Recording data: What did you find out?

Conclude this session by having each pair make a drawing or construct a representation of what they counted and how many they found. Provide as wide a variety of materials as you can. Some students may draw a picture showing every single chair they counted. Others might glue buttons on a piece of paper to show the coats they counted. If students used interconnecting cubes, they could connect their cubes into a tower and make a sign for what the tower shows. A display of many of these towers would allow students to compare all their data.

Students can write or dictate sentences to describe their picture or model. ■

66 99 DIALOGUE BOX
Everyone has coats!

Jesse's dad is wondering how many cookies to send. What could he count to figure out how many there are in this class?

SUMI: The pictures we made.

JESSE: He could just look at the round table where all our things are that we made with the buttons and stuff.

The models and pictures you made to show how many of you there are? Great. That would really be helpful. OK. And if he didn't see that, or he wanted to check something else, what else in the room could he count?

LILUE: How many coats there are.

What do people think about that?

RICH: It wouldn't work because if the kids were out they'd be wearing their coats.

SIMON: Not if we were at music.

BARBARA: Or if we went to lunch and it was raining and we weren't going out, we wouldn't take our coats.

CAL: But maybe everyone isn't wearing a coat, like it's a warm day.

FERNANDO: In the summer it wouldn't work.

How about a day like today?

ALEXEI: Yeah, everyone has coats.

JANE: I don't. I have a sweater.

KYLE: Me, too. I have a sweater.

JINNY: I have a jacket.

DAVID: That's the same thing as a coat.

JANE: You could count coats and sweaters.

JINNY: And jackets.

KARIMA: Right, 'cause everyone wore something.

OK. So on some days coats and jackets and sweaters would work. Who has a different idea?

FELICE: He could count the desks.

MELISSA: Or count the chairs by the desks.

Count the desks, or the chairs? Would that give a pretty close idea of how many of you there are?

MARK: Not if you count all the chairs, because some of them are by the table.

[Dialogue Box continued]

ALEXEI: If he counted those, there'd be extra. He'd have too many.

DANNY: You could just count the chairs by the desks.

Do you think he might just count the chairs by the desks?

DANNY: Yeah, because you can kind of tell that those are with the desks and that the other ones by the table are just for a reading group or something.

FELICE: So it's better to count the desks.

ERICA: But there's an extra desk in the painting corner.

LYNNE: And there's another one in the dress-up corner.

FELICE: You can tell, though, that that's not a person's desk. You'd just count the desks with people's stuff in them.

KYLE: That's how you can tell —look in and see if there's a kid's stuff there, and then you count it.

OK. So the desks or the chairs could help give a pretty close estimate of how many students are in here. What else could he use?

KAREN: The birthday chart.

How would the birthday chart help?

KAREN: Count the cakes.

You mean count these cakes [*points to chart, where there is one cake for each month*]. **Would that help him know how many students are in this class?**

STUDENTS [*variously*]: Yes . . . No . . . Yes . . .

Who can help us figure this out?

SUMI: Not the cakes, that's like January, February.

Show us.

SUMI [*going up to chart*]: See, like this is for January, this is for February, but these are the *kids* [*points to names of students listed under each month*]. See, you can count the kids.

OK, you could count the kids. Let's get some other ideas.

CAL: But it wouldn't be right.

What wouldn't be?

CAL: Cause we didn't put on Matt yet, when he came.

ROSALIE: Yeah, so it's only 22.

We better put Matt on the birthday chart so we don't forget his birthday! But suppose it was like that, and Matt wasn't on it. Would it still give a close number when someone counted?

ROSALIE: It would be 22 'cause we had 22 kids before Matt.

JESSE: It would just be one off.

FERNANDO: But if he was sending cookies there wouldn't be enough.

LILUE: We could share.

PAUL: That wouldn't be fair, because then some kids would get a whole cookie and some would get a half.

SIMON: Maybe someone would be absent, so it would be 22.

JANE: Sometimes a few kids are absent, like today when we counted we only had 21, so then there would be enough.

JINNY: But if everyone were here, someone wouldn't get a cookie.

GUSTAVE: He might send extras. He might count 22 and then get a few more in case some of them fall on the floor or get crushed up.

That's an interesting idea. He could estimate how many students there are in here by counting something like the birthday chart— estimating is getting a number that's pretty close but might not be exactly the number— and then add a few extra just in case.

CAL: Then if there's extra we could have another one.

MATT: There could be one for Ms. Carlson if there was an extra. ■

✎ TEACHER NOTE
On estimating

Estimation is a big part of all mathematics. Sometimes estimates are used to check that an exact calculation is reasonable, but often estimates are important in their own right. An estimate can be the complete solution to a mathematical problem, both in everyday life and in mathematics. In fact, the whole field of statistics is built on estimates. When a poll shows that a candidate is leading the field with 65% of the vote, or a newspaper reports the median income in your community, this figure is a carefully formulated estimate of the "real" number.

Primary grade students can begin to understand what an estimate is and why it is useful. An estimate is a careful approximation of some quantity. To get an estimate, we use whatever we do know to get a number that is close enough for our purposes. Sometimes, these estimates can be quite rough. At other times we want to get a very close estimate. Consider these two examples:

▼ Six people are coming to dinner, and you are going to serve chicken. You figure that each person will eat about a half pound of chicken, but you want to make sure you have enough, so you'll buy an extra pound. That will be fine, because you'd rather overestimate in case someone is a big eater. You can always use the leftovers.

▼ You have been wanting to replace the tile in your bathroom, and you see some tile on sale that is exactly what you want. You don't want to pay for more than you need. On the other hand, the salesperson told you that at the sale price it is selling out fast, and they don't intend to restock this tile. You don't want to take the chance that you will get the bathroom partly tiled and not be able to get any more. In this case, you estimate the number of tiles you will need quite carefully.

It is important to measure how adequate the estimate is by referring to how it is going to be used, not by how close it is to the "real" number. In the chicken example, you would not say you made a bad estimate because it turned out that one person was a vegetarian and didn't eat any chicken. You would still feel you had prepared adequately for the situation. For your purposes, 3 pounds was not a better estimate than 4 pounds, even though that was closer to what people actually ate. On the other hand, if you bought 150 tiles, and it turned out you actually needed 155, you would be unhappy with your estimate, whereas if you actually used 140, you would probably be quite pleased, even though your estimate was not as close to the "real" number.

In the classroom, it is important not to set up situations in which estimation is really a disguised search for the "real" number. For example, in the Dialogue Box, *Everyone has coats!* (page 33), the teacher did not criticize the suggestion about desks, even though there were more desks than children in the classroom. Rather, she supported students in trying to figure out how they would consider the desks if they used them as a basis for their count.

Some students will not be happy with this idea, even though you have set the tone for finding a good estimate rather than an exact answer. For example, one first grader counted and recounted a display of pictures and was very unhappy when she kept getting 21 rather than 23, which was the number of students in the class. She wanted to be "right," and the teacher had to work to convince her to record 21 for her picture. Later, in the class discussion, students talked about which of these estimates they would trust if they didn't know the real number, how they would check one estimate with another, and how they would probably make a few extra cookies anyway, just to be safe. If these strategies are used for estimation, then estimates of 21 or 22 are both perfectly adequate estimates for the situation; 22 is not necessarily a "better" estimate even though it is closer to the actual number. ■

✎ TEACHER NOTE
Working in pairs

Kindergarten and first grade children are often just beginning to move from parallel or simultaneous play to cooperative play. Working in pairs is a good way to get started. However, figuring out how to collaborate on a task is not always easy. Consider this example from a first grade classroom:

David and Alexei start working together to count the number of names on the birthday chart. They sit on the rug in front of the chart with a pile of buttons and a paper cup. Alexei counts silently and takes a button from the floor with each count. She gets interrupted by David, who is counting out loud as he moves buttons from the pile to another pile. David runs out of buttons and tries to get more from Alexei, and Alexei gets more and more impatient as she has to start over and over again.

After a few minutes of this activity, the teacher stops the class to discuss strategies for counting. Students talk about what they are counting, what they are using to count with, how they are moving the counters (e.g., start with all the counters on my desk, put them into the cup every time we count something), and what they do with the leftover counters so they do not get these mixed up with the ones they have counted. David and Alexei are able to use this information to make a new plan. This time,

they decided to count coats. Their teachers tells them they can take the coats off the hooks if they need to, since there is often more than one coat on a hook. David and Alexei take all the coats off, then hang them up one at a time. Each time David hangs one coat, Alexei puts one button into their paper cup.

Find an appropriate time during this investigation for students to share their strategies for counting and working together. Here are some other strategies students have described:

▼ "We counted the names by twos up to 24. Then we put 24 counters in the bag and kept the leftovers in our hands."

▼ "Barbara counted the chairs. Then we took turns putting the beans into a cup."

▼ "We went around and touched every desk. Every time Rosalie touched a desk, we put a straw in the bag. We gave the extras back to Ms. Carlson. Then we counted our straws."

▼ "Simon and I counted the birthday names. First we counted for October—it was 5, so we put 5 buttons in the bag. Then we counted 4 for November and put 4 buttons in. And we kept going like that." ■

SESSION 2 AND 3 ACTIVITIES

Interpreting the data: An estimate for our class

Begin by having students share and demonstrate their strategies for counting. See the Teacher Note, *Working in pairs* (at left).

Now ask students what they think the hypothetical cookie-providing parent would have decided about how many students are in this class. Their representations of their results should be in sight for reference. You may also want to list on the board all the students' counting results:

coats	22, 21
lunch boxes	15
birthday names	22, 22
desks	25, 27, 25
chairs	26

So if Jesse's dad had come in and had counted these things, what do you think he could figure out about how many students are in our class?

Following are other questions you might use in this discussion:

What was the lowest count? Why do you think that one was so low? What was the highest count? Why was that one so high? What numbers come up often? Why do you think so? What about things for which you found

different numbers? **What might have happened there?**

For more about this issue, see the Teacher Note, *Is it 21 or 22?* (page 39).

Students contribute their ideas about which counts give good estimates ("He'd know that everyone doesn't bring a lunch box, so I think he wouldn't use that") and what would make sense for the parent to conclude. In this case, knowing that there were *about 22 students* or *between 20 and 25 students* would be useful information.

This list of common objects in the classroom also provides appropriate language experience for these students. Throughout this unit, much of the discussion and recording of data lends itself to integrating language development with mathematics.

Considering the problem: Nobody here, so how many are there?

Now you're going to be detectives in another classroom. You're going to try to figure out how many students are in another class by counting things in their room, just the way you did here. You're going to make an estimate and then decide how many cookies to bring to that classroom as a treat. It will be a surprise, so you need to count when the class isn't there.

☛ If you cannot supply real cookies (or, even better, make cookies with your students), you can still carry out this activity as a hypothetical situation ("Let's see how many cookies we think would be the right number for their classroom," or simply, "We're going to try to figure out how many students are in their classroom").

Make plans with your students about what they will count and how they will keep track. They can use methods of counting similar to those they used to count things in their own classroom. Keep in mind that some young students may still be working on the idea of how one set of things can represent another (see the Teacher Note, *On the verge of a big idea*, page 39). This may be a good time for students to share their ideas about how to keep track when they are counting. See the Teacher Note, *Working in pairs* (page 36).

Have students help you make a list of what could be counted, and assign these items to pairs of students. It's a good idea to have some things preassigned, and then encourage students to choose some additional things to count in the neighboring classroom once they get in there. After all, the other classroom may contain some things that no one has thought about; you cannot know for sure in advance what might be useful to count. As before, it's fine if more than one pair of students counts the same thing.

Collecting the data: A visit to another classroom

Group the students in pairs. Each pair needs to have a set of materials, such as the con-

crete objects used in Session 1, to help them count. If each pair will be counting several things, they will need paper and pencil to record all their counts.

Take students to visit the other classroom when it is empty so they can collect their data.

Organizing the data: Comparing the counts

This time each pair of students makes the same kind of representation so that the counts can be easily compared. Choose either squared paper or interlocking cubes. That is, each pair of students either cuts out a strip of squares or builds a tower of interlocking cubes corresponding to the number of things they counted.

Make a display of these representations so that they can be viewed and compared. For example:

Erica and Felice:

Cubbies ⬚⬚⬚⬚⬚⬚⬚⬚⬚⬚⬚⬚⬚⬚⬚⬚⬚⬚⬚⬚

Coats ⬚⬚⬚⬚⬚⬚⬚⬚⬚⬚⬚⬚⬚⬚⬚⬚⬚⬚⬚⬚⬚⬚⬚

Karen and Kyle:

Lunch boxes ⬚⬚⬚⬚⬚⬚⬚⬚⬚⬚⬚⬚

Birthday names ⬚⬚⬚⬚⬚⬚⬚⬚⬚⬚⬚⬚⬚⬚⬚⬚⬚⬚⬚⬚⬚⬚⬚

Also compile a list of the students' data. For example:

Erica and Felice	cubbies	20
	coats	23
Karen and Kyle	lunch boxes	12
	birthday names	23

Extensions

▼ In one kindergarten class, the students loved the idea of being "detectives," and detective play spilled over into the dress-up corner.

▼ Instead of cookies, you might provide a treat like peanuts (in the shell) for the other class so that each student will get more than one. Then, once your class has decided on an estimate of how many are in the other class, some of your students can work together to count out the total number of peanuts needed. This problem in multiplication (e.g., 22 students times 5 peanuts each) provides a nice exploration in counting and finding patterns for some students at this age level. For example, students might lay out 22 rows of 5 buttons each, then put these on a hundred chart (page 67 or 69), one for each number, and put the "leftover" buttons on a second hundred chart. Some first graders are fascinated with numbers this large, even if they can only barely grasp a sense of this quantity. It is a good idea to put each group of peanuts in a small bag or paper cup, so that students can see that there are the same number of bags/cups as the number they decided on for their estimate of the number of students. ■

Susan Jo's Peanut Butter Balls (uncooked)

1 cup peanut butter
1 cup honey or molasses
1½ cups powdered milk

Add two or more of these options:

1 cup raisins
1 cup sunflower seeds (hulled)
1 cup sesame seeds, toasted
½ cup soy grits

Coverings
ground nuts, toasted sesame seeds, sunflower seeds, wheat germ, coconut, soy grits

Directions

1. Mix all ingredients together, including any of the optional ingredients you choose.

2. Shape into balls.

3. Roll balls in one of the coverings.

Makes 3-4 dozen balls.

✎ TEACHER NOTE
Is it 21 or 22?

Throughout this investigation, situations will come up in which different students counted the same thing and arrived at different numbers. This is tricky for a teacher to handle, because one of the counts is clearly "right" and one is not. However, simply verifying which one is right may not improve student understanding of numbers and counting. In fact, there is no evidence that the student with the more accurate count has a deeper understanding.

When this situation arises, focus on strategies for keeping track of a count, reasons for losing count, and ways to double-check. Involve students in thinking about why there are differences:

▼ "The coats were really hard to count because a lot of them were on the floor, and we kept having to pick them up, and then we'd forget which ones we'd counted."

▼ "We got 27 for the desks, but Lynne and Maya got 25 and so did Matt and Karima. But we think maybe they didn't count the two desks the painting stuff is on."

The fact is, it's really easy for any of us to be off by 1 or 2 when we are counting. How many times have you recounted something and gotten a different number? Students should understand that it is easy to miscount but that there are strategies—such as recounting, having someone else count, making sure we say the number at the same time we touch an object, moving an object from one spot to another as we count—which help us be more sure of our count.

And, finally, a close count may be good enough for some purposes. In this case, if one count of chairs is 23 and one is 24, both these numbers give us a pretty good estimate of the number of students in the class. ■

✎ TEACHER NOTE
On the verge of a big idea

Throughout this unit, you will find that students in your class are continually discovering new ideas about number. Not all students will make the same discoveries at the same time. When a young child is on the verge of understanding something new, you will notice excitement, engagement—even obsession—with this new idea. For example, when a 4-year-old first learns to say the number-string, "1, 2, 3, 4, 5, 6, 7, 8, 9, 10," she is likely to go around pointing and saying these words, proudly letting everyone know she can count to 10, even if the objects she counts don't match the words she is saying. A 5-year-old becomes fascinated with the fact that he has 5 fingers and he is 5 years old. Other students become engaged as they learn to recognize patterns on dice—that a square of 4 dots with one in the middle is always 5—or how to coordinate the counting words, one-for-one, with objects. Many students discover that "the numbers go on forever," and become passionate about counting as high as they can.

Part of the difficult job of the teacher of kindergarten and first grade children is to find out what number and counting ideas each child is working on and to provide many opportunities for children to consolidate and extend old ideas and to explore new ones. Luckily, many of the same activities can provide counting experiences for children who are doing very different kinds of mathematical work. For example, given a hundred chart, some students may use it to try to count to 100, while others might cover up numbers between 1 and 10 and try to guess the numbers that are covered.

For all these counting activities, it's fine that students will be participating at different levels. It gives them the opportunity to hear new ideas from each other, and they will all gradually increase their number sense and familiarity with number symbols through continuous exposure.

In the investigation *Nobody here, nobody there*, some students may persist in counting things that are not completely related to the task at hand—which is estimating the number of students in a class. For example, Sumi, a student in a kindergarten class, suggested that they count things like the ABC cards strung along the chalkboard, the numbers on the clock, and the doors in the classroom. Kyle, a first grader, counted desks and chairs in the neighboring class, but then became absorbed in trying to count the numbers of marbles in a jar.

In each case you can easily see what the student wants to count, but it is more difficult to figure out what the student is thinking about. Sumi may not yet understand that you can get numerical information about one thing by counting something else. For instance, she might not know that, if there are pairs of forks and knives on a

table, counting the forks will also tell you how many knives there are. For her, the whole idea of estimating—getting an approximate idea—is foreign, because she does not know any way of obtaining numerical information other than directly counting something. Kyle, whose behavior might at first look the same as Sumi's, may also be more interested in the act of counting than in the problem of estimation, but for a different reason. Perhaps he understands the task perfectly well, but has recently learned the pattern for counting beyond 20 and loves the challenge of counting something that looks like "a lot."

Your challenge is to constantly try to understand how each child is thinking about numbers, what are the "big ideas" with which that child is struggling, and what sort of task will involve that child in working with exactly that concept he or she is trying to conquer. ■

SESSION 4 ACTIVITIES

Interpreting the data and developing theories: How many students in the other class?

Look with your students at the data they collected. What do they think is a good estimate for the number of students in the other class? Use the same kinds of discussion questions suggested in Session 2, when you looked at the data for your own class. Encourage the students to make statements such as, "There must be at least . . . " or "There probably are not more than . . . ."

If your students are planning to make or buy cookies for the other class, they will have an excellent reason for arriving at a good estimate.

Publishing findings: Reporting to the other class

Arrange with the other teacher for a time to take your students back to the other classroom to report on what they did, what their estimate is, and what their reasons are for the estimate. (Bring the cookies or peanuts, if you decided to provide some.) In one school a kindergarten collaborated with a first grade that was also using the unit. Each did their count of the other class and analyzed their data. Then they met together to share results. At the end of the discussion the real numbers were revealed and cookies were shared all around.

An alternative way to finish this investigation is to write a letter to the other class, sharing the students' findings and asking for a reply that tells how many students there actually are in the other class.

A final question for your students to consider, once they know the actual count: How reasonable was their estimate? Did it work well for figuring out the number of cookies or peanuts they needed for the other class?

Extensions

▼ Students may enjoy using calculators to count with. For students who are comfortable counting directly and using concrete objects to represent their counts, counting using the calculator is an appropriate introduction to calculator use. See the Teacher Note, *Young children can use calculators* (following).

▼ If you have a bunch of blankets or a large closet in your room and a willing outside participant as guinea pig, you can have all the children hide, then ask the person to come into the classroom and estimate how many are in the class. The children then emerge and discuss with your guest how he or she made the estimate and why it was close or far off. You could do this several times with several different people throughout the year.

▼ In this investigation, students seem to become interested in collecting further information about themselves and the other class. For example, one class decided they wanted to know how many boys and girls there were in the other class, so they included this question in their letter. Be alert for questions like these that might lead to further data collection activities. ■

Young children can use calculators

It is appropriate for kindergarten and first grade students to begin having experiences with calculators, and we encourage you to make calculators available throughout this unit. Even though young students do not yet have a grasp of all the numbers and operations they can produce on the calculator, the calculator is simply one more tool they can use to expand their repertoire about what kinds of numbers there are, what numbers look like, and how numbers are sequenced. A calculator can become a familiar part of their environment early, along with cubes, blocks, counters, and hundred charts.

As with any new material, students will need time to "mess around" with the calculator and make their own discoveries before they will be ready to learn about particular keys and about sequences that make particular things happen. We recommend that calculators be available at all times and that you set aside some small-group work time to help students learn how to make a number that they want on the calculator, how to clear the screen, and how to count using the calculator.

Young children can use a calculator for counting by adding 1 each time they count.

For most calculators, start with the calculator at 0, then press the keys for +, 1, and = to get the next number. Students do not need to understand the operation of addition to do this. They can learn that "this is the way the calculator makes 1 more."

Of course, it is not easy for all young students to coordinate this sequence of keys or to coordinate a +1 with each count of an object—any more than it is always easy for them to coordinate the numbers they are saying with the objects they are counting. Since most calculators do not keep a record of your previous entries, there is no way to tell how far off you are when you lose track of your count. Of course, there is often no way to tell what your error was if you are counting real objects, either, except by going back and counting again. Regardless, many students in the early primary grades will enjoy playing around with the +1 sequence. This will be one more way for them to see the sequence of numbers in order.

Some students became very involved in exploring the +1 sequence. One student said at first, regretfully, "Gee, too bad it can't go over 9." She was delighted when she found it could handle 10, 11, and higher numbers. The +1 sequence on the calculator is another route for students to follow in exploring the idea that "the numbers go on forever."

Students will need experience operating the calculator before they can use it in real situations. If you want students to use the calculator for counting in the investigations *Nobody here, nobody there* and *Counting noses,* they need to have some experience with it before those sessions.

If you are interested in using calculators with your class, one good resource is *The Calculator Mathematics Books*, designed by the University of Chicago School Mathematics Project for students in grades 1–3 (available from Everyday Math Tools, 1007 Church St., Suite 306, Evanston, IL 60201). ■

INVESTIGATION OVERVIEW

What happens

Students investigate how many noses there are in the classroom. They develop a plan for counting the noses, and represent the result by making a display of interlocking cubes and/or noses made out of clay. The group then lists all the body parts that, like noses, are in a one-to-one correspondence with the number of students.

The class next explores body parts that come in pairs, collecting, counting, and recording data about such parts as legs and ears. A large display chart of pairs of eyes, hands, or feet is constructed. Students explore counting by twos with a calculator and work in small groups to make their own pictorial representations of one of the body parts.

The number of sessions required for these activities will vary from three to five, and pacing will depend on which issues about counting and number are most important for your students. If you are teaching young kindergarten and first grade students, you will probably want to conduct this investigation as it is outlined here, spending at least one whole session on one-to-one correspondence (Session 1). For these younger students, you might spend only two sessions on two-to-one correspondence, selecting from the activities in Sessions 2, 4, and 5. If, however, your students are quite comfortable with one-to-one correspondence, you may want to combine Sessions 1 and 2 and move into two-to-one correspondence by the end of the first session. For these students, you can easily spend three or more sessions on the activities described in Sessions 2, 4, and 5. An additional session, Session 3, is recommended for small-group work with the calculator. If you wish, spread this small-group work throughout the investigation.

What to plan ahead of time

▼ Provide interlocking cubes, such as Unifix cubes, and/or clay for making representations of the number of noses in the class (Session 1).

▼ Provide large index cards (5-by-8-inch) for drawing eyes, or 8-1/2-by-11-inch paper for tracing hands or feet (Session 2).

▼ Clear some wall space in the classroom for the large display(s) of eyes, hands, or feet (Session 2).

▼ If you choose the tracing hands or feet option, you may want to enlist volunteer parents or older students to help with the tracing (Session 2).

▼ Make calculators available for experimenting and for counting by twos (throughout; in particular, Session 3).

▼ Provide a variety of materials for making representations of body parts that come in pairs. Include large (11-by-17-inch) drawing paper, crayons, squared paper (page 71 or 73), stick-on notes, materials students can paste onto paper, scissors, and glue or paste (Sessions 4-5).

Important mathematical ideas

Matching one-to-one. When two sets of objects are matched, one object in one set with exactly one object in the other set, each set has the same number of objects. This one-to-one correspondence means that if there are 26 students, and each student has exactly one nose, then there are 26 noses.

Matching two-to-one. If there are exactly two objects in one set for each object in another set, there is a two-to-one correspondence. For 26 students, each of whom has two arms, there will be twice the number of arms as students. This early exploration of many-to-one counts is the foundation upon which a great deal of mathematics is built, including multiplication, division, and ratios.

Counting by twos. As students count by twos in a variety of situations, they will begin to notice the patterns of the even numbers.

Counting above 20. The names of the numbers occur in a regular way in each decade, starting with the twenties. Some students will already know this pattern; others will be working hard to learn it.

Students who are right in the middle of learning this pattern will often count, "25, 26, 27, 28, 29 . . . what's the next one? [*someone prompts, "30"*] . . . oh, yeah, 30, 31, 32, 33 . . ." At this point, the child knows the interior pattern and is learning the names of the decades—20, 30, 40, and so forth.

Visualizing quantities. As students learn the names of the counting numbers, they simultaneously begin to visualize "how big" those numbers are. They need to do this in many situations, with concrete objects and materials of all kinds, so that they are continually developing their sense of the size of quantities in comparison to other quantities.

Using concrete materials to record data. The first step toward making a permanent record of data is to use one object for each item counted, to make a concrete representation of the real things. While this kind of representation seems straightforward to adults, it is still, for young children, one step more abstract than counting the actual items.

Making pictures to record data. Making pictures as permanent records of the data students have collected lays the foundation for creating a variety of representations of data, including tallies, charts, and graphs. ■

SESSION 1 ACTIVITIES

Introducing the problem: How many noses?

Ask the students if they know what counting noses means. You might want to introduce the expression in a situational context such as:

A friend of mine had a big picnic at her house. She needed to know how many cups to bring outside, so before everybody sat down to eat, she told me that she "counted noses." What do you think she meant?

After a little discussion, focus on the phrase *counting noses* as an expression we sometimes use to mean we are going to find out how many people there are.

If we counted all the noses in the room, how many noses would there be?

Some students may know how many people are in the room, say 26, and be very sure that there will be 26 noses. Others may be less sure, even though they may parrot what they hear other students saying. For them, this investigation will be a chance to revisit the notion of one-to-one correspondence that they explored in the earlier investigation, *How many of us?* Accept all the students' answers and ask them why they think their predictions will work.

Collecting the data: Counting noses

Even those students who are most sure what the count will be always enjoy the activity of counting noses, a phrase they view as quite comical.

How can we make sure we count all the noses and don't leave anyone out?

Students may suggest using the actual people or using the self-portraits they made earlier. If some class members are absent, wait for students to bring up this issue and let them decide how to include these students in the count. After you have settled on a method, go ahead and do the nose count.

Representing the data: Making a permanent record

To make a permanent record of how many noses there are in the classroom, do one or both of the following:

▼ Each child takes an interlocking cube to represent his or her nose. Put all the cubes together to make a "tower of noses." Count these with the students.

▼ Every child makes a clay nose. When the noses are finished, line them up on a table or on the chalkboard ledge. Some students may enjoy writing the numerals, from 1 to the total class number, on index cards or stick-on notes to make labels for each nose.

Extending the investigation: If there are 26 noses . . .

Begin the discussion by asking students to confirm how many noses their representation (cubes or clay noses) shows. This is also a good time to compare the nose representation with other representations in the room—for example, the dot chart and self-portraits from the investigation, *How many of us?* If the number of children in the class has changed since one or more of these was made, the differences offer the opportunity for interesting discussion.

When students are agreed on the number of noses their representation shows, write on the chalkboard or on large chart paper something like the following:

> There are 26 noses in our class.

Ask students what other body parts there would be 26 of, if they counted them (see the Teacher Note, *Sensitive issues in dealing with parts of the body*, page 46). Write their suggestions on the list:

> There are 26 heads in our class.
> There are 26 stomachs in our class.
> There are 26 mouths in our class.

It is very likely that students will mention body parts that come in pairs ("There are more than 26 legs," "There are two each of nostrils"). You can note these remarks and tell students you will come back to them in the next session; or, if your students are very comfortable with the one-to-one correspondences you have been discussing, you may want to use such a remark as an opportunity to start a second list (see Session 2 Activities for details).

Extensions

▼ Use your "There are 26 noses" list to take attendance, each day counting a different one of the body parts students have mentioned.

▼ In this session, as in many of the others in this unit, there are opportunities for integrating the development of written and oral language into mathematics. You may want to use the "There are 26 noses" list for some language experience work. This list provides sight vocabulary in a meaningful context and uses a repetitive sentence structure that allows students to catch on to the pattern quickly. ■

“” DIALOGUE BOX
Counting noses

In this class, the students have made clay noses and just finish counting them.

So why were there 26 noses?

SUMI: Because everyone in the whole class made one and that is the same number as the kids in the class.

MATT: We made them and we counted them.

We counted them? And why did that mean there were 26?

MATT: Because they each had one nose and all the noses from 26 kids would equal 26 noses.

ALEXEI: If we counted everyone, there would be 28.

Why would there be 28?

ALEXEI: 26 noses, then you and Jesse's mother, 27, 28.

KAREN: We used to have 26, and then we had 27, and now we have 26 again.

How did that happen?

KAREN: Because first we had 26, and then Felice came, so that was 27.

LILUE: And then Jacqui left, so it was 26 again.

Here's the dot chart we made of how many we are. Do you think we could take our noses and put one nose onto every blue dot, and would there be the same number?

STUDENTS [*variously*]: Yes . . . No . . . Yes . . .

Who has a reason for their prediction?

ERICA: There have to be the same, noses and dots, because there's one dot for every person and one nose for every person.

KARIMA: But Jacqui was here when we did that [*points to the dot chart*].

FELICE: And I was here, too. Now we are 26. So 27 dots and 26 noses. ■

✎ TEACHER NOTE
Sensitive issues in dealing with parts of the body

Two sensitive issues may arise in your classroom. One, of course, is some general silliness about parts of the body that students think they are not supposed to mention in class, or “silly words” for some more private parts of the body. You will have to handle these remarks according to your own and your school's approach. We recommend a straightforward approach, emphasizing correct vocabulary, designed to dilute the silliness. Although the authors had anticipated this issue in trial versions of these materials, in fact, in test classrooms the students were so genuinely engaged in the mathematics of this investigation that discussion of private parts of the body never arose. However, that doesn't mean that it will not come up in your class, and you might want to think a bit in advance about how to keep the focus on the mathematics.

The other issue will arise in classrooms in which there are students who do not have the usual number of body parts; for example, a child who is missing an arm or several fingers. If this is the case in your classroom, you will already have talked with your class about the student's special needs so that, presumably, some matter-of-factness toward this child's differences will already have been established. In this investigation, the student's differences should be included in the discussion as a mathematical issue: If we are going to count arms, and Jesse has one, how will we make sure we get the right count? Depending on your own style and how well integrated Jesse has become, you can even make this a highlight of the mathematics: "We know we have 46 legs, but Lynne thinks something different will happen with arms. Who can predict how many arms we will have?" Such discussions are often much more uncomfortable for adults than for the children, including Jesse, who are likely to be genuinely interested in such a problem. ■

SESSION 2 ACTIVITIES

Introducing the problem: What's more than noses?

Open this session by reviewing the list you made during the last session, then refer to any of the observations students made about body parts that come in pairs (or raise the issue yourself).

Remember what Kyle said about nostrils? Do you think there are 26 nostrils in our class?

Ask students to discuss what they think and give their reasons.

Start a new list:

> We have more than 26 nostrils.
> We have more than 26 hands.
> We have more than 26 _____.

Take students' suggestions for any body part they have more than one of: eyes, hands, feet, ears, elbows, and so forth. Students may also mention parts that do not come in pairs, such as fingers, hair, and teeth. Include them on the list.

Collecting data: Things that come in twos

Pick one of the choices that come in twos (like legs) and ask the students to suggest some ways to find out exactly how many there would be in the class. Students may want to start with estimates of how many they think there are. If a few students know the exact number, be careful that their "correct" response does not overshadow the important thinking other students are doing. As students are talking, listen for and support the use of such phrases as *double*, *twice as many*, and *two for each*. These are important clues to students' understanding of two-to-one correspondence. See the Teacher Note, *Two-to-one correspondence* (page 48).

Settle on some method for doing the actual count. In one classroom, the teacher had students rest their legs on their desks. Then, as each pair of legs was counted, the student swung them under the desk. Needless to say, this active participation was enjoyed by all. You can think of other ways to dramatize the count. If students are counting ears, they could hold their hands (lightly, so they can still hear the count!) over their ears, then take them down as their ears are counted. The more clearly you can establish a physical movement that is linked with the counting, the more easily your students will be able to associate the numbers with the objects being counted.

You can limit your count to the students who are in class today, then add the absentees later, when students are convinced about the count of students who are physically present.

Record the number on the board:

There are 52 legs in our class.

Are there any other things that you think there are 52 of?

If you wish, count another body part to confirm the students' conjectures. This time you might want to give a greater emphasis to the even numbers as you count:

1, **2**, 3, **4**, 5, **6** . . .

Students enjoy participating in this rhythmic count, but keep in mind that they can become so wrapped up in the count, they no longer notice the correspondence of each number with an object being counted. See the Teacher Note, *Two-to-one correspondence* (following on this page).

Recording data: Making a large display of eyes, hands, or feet

Conclude this session with at least one of the following activities:

▼ Have each student draw his or her eyes on a large index card. (Note that this makes a nice two-to-one correspondence: two eyes to one card.) Provide a mirror, so that students who do not know the color of their eyes can see them.

▼ Have students make tracings of their hands or feet.

Make a large display of the eye cards or the hand or foot tracings. Pair the hands and feet so that all the right hands (or feet) are on the right and the left hands (or feet) are on the left. With the students, count the total. Write the numerals next to or on each of the objects (1 on the first left foot, 2 on the corresponding right foot, 3 on the next left foot, 4 on its matching right foot, and so forth). Ask students to dictate a sentence or two to explain the display.

Extensions

All kinds of counting and patterns that emphasize twos can be integrated into these activities. Students can build sequences in twos with colored blocks or tiles. Using squared paper (page 71 or 73), students can draw patterns that show twos (for example, one square blue, one square green; the next square blue, the next square green, and so on). If students use a section of squared paper with 5 rows of 5 squares each, they will find that the pattern is different from one that is made using an even number of squares in a row. Why is this? ■

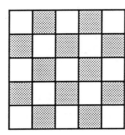 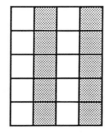

✎ *TEACHER NOTE*
Two-to-one correspondence

The relationships of *half* and *double* are key mathematical ideas. The two-to-one correspondence that students have noticed on their own bodies as well as in natural sharing activities ("two for you, two for me") is a relationship that leads to critical ideas about multiplication, division, and ratios. Forming pairs and counting by twos is also connected to later work in place value where a group of things can be counted as one group, although, at the same time, it still retains the value of the number of things it contains. Listen for student remarks that give insight into their understanding, such as these from first graders (26 students in their class):

▼ "There is a difference [between the two lists]. If we have only one of it on our body, then we have 26. If we have two of it, then we have 52."

▼ "There's two more each time, so it's double."

▼ "I think if you take away one leg of everybody, then you'll have 26."

Engage students in finding concrete ways of representing pairs so that they can see the two-to-one correspondence. For example, one pair of students used checkers. They made a line of 26 red checkers, then "kinged" them with 26 black checkers. Another group used

Unifix cubes. They built a tower of 23 cubes to show right hands, then another tower next to it to show left hands.

Find ways to count in pairs whenever you have the opportunity. At first, use all the numbers while counting ("1, 2, 3, 4, 5, 6"). Eventually, you can emphasize the even numbers as you count so that students begin to hear the pattern of the odd and even numbers and feel the rhythm of counting by twos:

1, **2**, 3, **4**, 5, **6** . . .

Some teachers also use hand clapping and other physical rhythmic movements. For example, you might take attendance by twos, counting by ones (1, 2, 3, 4 . . .) while students clap only on the even numbers. Some of your students may actually begin counting by twos, saying "2" for two objects, "4" for the next two objects, and so forth. However, do not rush students into skipping numbers. If they get confused ("2, 4, 8, 6 . . . "), encourage them to verbalize the "in-between numbers" under their breath.

Keep in mind that students may lose track of the number-object correspondence as they become involved in the rhythm of the count. Just as they learned the number chant "1, 2, 3, 4, 5, 6, 7, 8, 9, 10" before they could actually count objects, they can learn the "counting by twos" chant without understanding anything about what they are counting. This is not terrible. Many students

will enjoy simply learning the number pattern. But, as always, be aware that just because students can say the numbers, it does not mean that they understand the quantities these numbers represent. Students need continued experience with counting, in many situations, with diverse objects and materials, as they explore the complexity of the number system.

Work with two-to-one relationships may lead some students to consider many-to-one relationships. For example, three first graders worked together to find out the number of toes in the class. First one of them counted all the student desks in the classroom. The teacher did not understand what that student was doing, but left the group to work out its method. Then the threesome sat on the floor and made groups of ten crayons. They knew how many groups to make by the number of desks they had counted! Finally they counted all the crayons (both by ones and, with some help, by tens) and reported back to the rest of the class. In fact, the high point of this investigation occurred when the trio poured out all 260 crayons onto a table. So many toes! The rest of the students were visibly surprised. ■

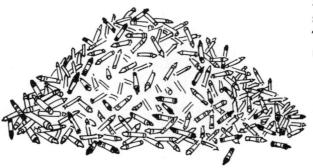

SESSION 3 ACTIVITIES

Counting with the calculator: Small-group work

Meet with small groups to further explore calculator use. If you have students who are already comfortable with using the calculator to count (using the +, 1, and = keys), ask them if they can figure out a way to make the calculator count by twos. Let students experiment, then show them the +, 2, = sequence. You may want to pair students to maximize both understanding of the process and small-motor coordination. Sometimes young children know what they want to do but cannot make their fingers do it. Other children may be able to manipulate the keys very well but may not be able to keep in mind the sequence.

Be aware that work with the calculator should be dropped if it is only a frustrating experience. These activities are meant to be a gentle introduction. Most students will be intrigued with this piece of adult technology and will enjoy trying different things, but there is certainly no reason to push them to master a particular sequence of keys. For a story of one 6-year-old's experience, see the Teacher Note, *Erica and the calculator* (page 50). ■

Erica and the calculator

Not-quite-6-year-old Erica had been fiddling with the calculator, mostly just entering numbers. She had also been very interested in the work on body parts that come in pairs. When her teacher showed her how to use the +, 2, and = keys to count up people's eyes, she immediately counted her own and her friend Rosalie's. She saw the 4 on the calculator screen, then counted on her fingers to see if the calculator's answer was right: "It's right! How does it do that?"

Erica began shaking the calculator, as if there might be something inside to count with. She began adding in more people's eyes. In the beginning, she kept checking out the answers with her fingers, but then became completely engaged with examining the bigger and bigger numbers.

After experimenting with the twos for a while, she finally said, "I wish there was a 10 on here. Then you could add up people's fingers." The teacher asked her how she would write a 10 (she knew how), and then showed her how to make it on the calculator by pushing the 1 first, and then the 0, just as she had written it. She started with her own 10 fingers, then carefully added 10 as she named each person in her family. Each time she looked at the numbers and read them in amazement. She said, "You know

how many there are altogether by looking at this!" After various counting episodes like this one, Erica would carry the calculator around with her, not clearing the screen, so that she could show her results to other students. ■

SESSION 4 AND 5 ACTIVITIES

Representing the data: Inventing pictures

For these activities, students work in pairs. Each group chooses a body part that comes in twos, such as ears, and makes a representation on paper of how many of these are in the room today. (If some class members are absent, students can choose to add their parts to the count as well.) Encourage students to draw, color, or cut and paste the number of objects they need.

Some students will make representations that are directly pictorial, although this task may become tedious (drawing 26 pairs of legs can take a long time). Others may invent versions of tallying, using a symbol such as a line or a circle to represent each object. Some students may want to use squared paper and color in the appropriate number of squares. Some may want to write the numerals next to their pairs, although this is certainly not a requirement.

Leave this task as open-ended as possible, so that students can choose their own methods. Encourage them to talk with you about how they are keeping track of the number of things they are counting and how they know that is the number in the room today.

A few children may want to pursue counts of fingers or toes. For an example, see the end of the Teacher Note, *Two-to-one correspondence* (page 48).

These pictures are the beginning of student work in making a permanent record of their data, leading to later work with tallies, charts, and graphs. See the Teacher Note, *Inventing pictures of the data* (following). Students' pictures can become part of your display for this investigation.

Extension

Apply these same ideas to investigations of animals or other objects that have regular many-to-one correspondences. For example, if you have a fish tank, there is a one-to-one correspondence of tails to fish and a two-to-one correspondence of eyes to fish, but there may not be a regular correspondence of fins to fish, if you have a number of different species. Rabbits, guinea pigs, and gerbils give you opportunities to deal with counting by fours, as do the wheels on toy cars and trucks. ■

✎TEACHER NOTE
Inventing pictures of the data

When students invent their own ways of representing their data, both now and in later grades, they often come up with wonderfully individual pictures or graphs that powerfully communicate the meaning of the data. Starting with pictures that are virtually direct representations of their data, such as the chart of pairs of eyes you made with the whole class, students will gradually move to

representations that are partly picture, partly graph. When they are older, they will add more standard graphs and tables to their repertoire.

In this unit, we focus on the use of concrete materials and pictures as modes of representation. In the *Counting noses* investigation, some students will begin to develop slightly more abstract representations, using a line or a circle or some other symbol to stand for the objects they are counting. Even when they move to this next level of abstraction, students' pictures or picture-graphs will not

us and all the people visiting today

necessarily follow the conventions of graph-making that adults would use. For instance, the pictures may not be all the same size or lined up so that it is easy to compare different groups. In the *Birthdays* investigation, students are introduced to a simple form of bar graph for comparing the number of students born in each month. In this graph, the fact that each cell of the graph is identified by a student's name helps students link the graph to the data it shows. However, when students are pushed to adopt the conventions of what graphs are "supposed"

to look like, they often produce mundane bar graphs which, for them, no longer communicate anything about their data.

Encourage students to create their own pictures and picture-graphs throughout their work in this unit. Through constructing their own representations, students become more familiar with their data, with numerical relationships, and with the connection between the action of counting, the objects that they count, and the symbols that represent these quantities. ∎

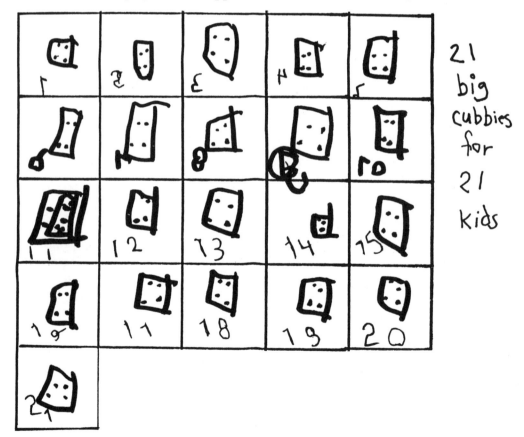

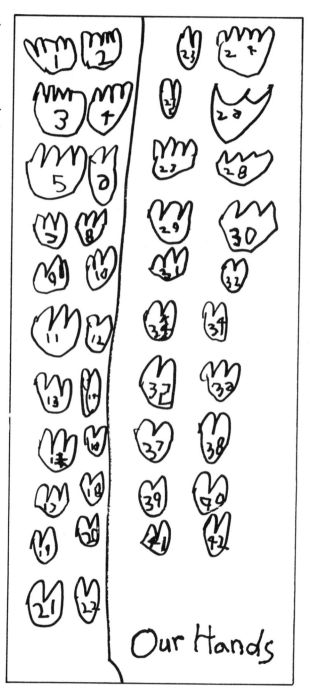

OUR AGES

INVESTIGATION OVERVIEW

What happens

Students use a variety of methods to represent and describe their own ages. Then they collect information about the ages of people in their families. Each student represents the ages of family members through a "family portrait" and by locating the ages on a hundred board.

The students construct and discuss a chart showing the ages of themselves and their siblings. In another session, they find ways to compare the ages of the oldest people in their data. An optional activity for first grade classes involves the creation of a giant chart showing all the age data they have collected.

The activities take five or six class sessions of about 45 minutes each.

What to plan ahead of time

▼ Provide a variety of materials with which students can show their ages, including squared paper, stick-on notes, interlocking cubes, and other counting materials, such as buttons or chips (Session 1).

▼ Arrange for students to find out the ages of their family members. Even though you may have some of this information in school records, it is important to let the students find it out for themselves. Duplicate Student Sheet 1 (page 65) and, if you wish, the letter to parents (page 63) for each student to take home (between Sessions 1 and 2).

▼ Provide drawing materials for students to make pictures of their families (Sessions 2 and 3).

▼ Provide a hundred board for each student (Sessions 2 and 3). You can duplicate one of the boards provided with this unit (pages 67 and 69) or use commercial laminated or plastic hundred boards. Students enjoy using the hundred board grids into which Unifix cubes or square plastic frames can be placed to mark special numbers.

▼ Provide a supply of interlocking cubes, such as Unifix cubes. You will need about 50 for each small group of four or five students in Session 3 and about 200 for each small group in Session 5. (If there is a lot of grandparent data, you may need more.) As a substitute for cubes, provide scissors and squared paper with small squares (page 71) so that students can cut out "towers" to represent their own ages and the ages of the oldest people in their families. If you use this method in Session 5, students will also need transparent tape to connect pieces in order to make their towers tall enough.

▼ Plan how to schedule small-group work. For much of the work in this investigation, students will be more engaged by the meaning of the numbers if they work in small groups to compare the ages of people in their families. You can play an important role if you are available to meet with each group to pose questions and encourage discussion. You may want to meet with small groups to work on the hundred board representations while others continue working on their family pictures (Sessions 2, 3, and 5).

▼ On a large piece of paper, prepare a number line (either vertical or horizontal), going from 0 to about 20 or 25, high enough to accommodate the ages of all the students' siblings (Session 4).

▼ Provide stick-on dots or stick-on notes in three different colors (Session 4).

▼ Provide 3-by-5-inch index cards or stick-on notes for labeling towers (Session 5).

▼ Prepare a large number line from 0 to the highest age in your students' data (optional, Session 6). You can put together three pieces of chart paper to do this, and you will need to clear some wall space! Plan the number line so that it will accommodate the size of stick-on notes or dots you plan to use.

▼ Provide stick-on notes or stick-on dots in at least five colors—though students may come up with ideas that will require more colors (optional, Session 6). Stick-on notes (the kind that can be put on and peeled off paper, such as Post-it notes) work best, since they are easy to rearrange. As an alternative, students can color in spaces on the chart, although this makes mistakes harder to correct.

Important mathematical ideas

Comparing several categories of data. Some data collection questions beginning with the words "How many . . . " can be answered with a single number. But questions that begin "How many more . . . " or "How many less . . . " require categorizing the data so that the number of items at each value can be compared. In earlier investigations, students have mostly collected single counts of something—the number of students in a class, the number of ears they all have. Now, in this investigation, students *compare* the numbers of 5-, 6-, and 7-year-olds in their class, or the ages of themselves, their brothers, and their sisters.

Displaying information about several categories. Students construct different representations that allow them to compare categories, including bar graphs and tallies.

Using numbers that stand for quantities you cannot count directly. In the earlier parts of this unit, students have dealt with people and objects they could count directly. In this investigation, they deal with age, a somewhat more abstract count. Age, as we use it here, is a count of years, and years cannot be touched and counted directly. When a 5-year-old says, "I'm five," she may know that the label "five" applies to her, but may not associate it with the five years it represents.

Finding and comparing numbers on a hundred board. Through working with the hundred board and locating numbers on it, students explore the structure, order, and patterns of the number system: All the 30s are in a row, all the "zero numbers" go down one side of the board, and so forth. Many students will at first count from the beginning of the board to locate any number or will simply look over the board randomly. As students gain experience, they will become familiar with patterns that help them locate numbers more quickly. These patterns will later connect to ideas about place value and the structure of our number system.

Displaying information to show both values and categories. Students encounter a more complex kind of representation when they display the ages of themselves, their sisters, and their brothers. This graph shows two dimensions of the students' data—age (e.g., 5 or 20) and category (e.g., brother or sister)—at the same time. ■

SESSION 1 ACTIVITIES

Introducing the problem: How old are people in our families?

Tell students that they will be collecting information about the ages of all the people in their families and that the class will be looking together at ages of brothers, sisters, mothers, fathers, and possibly others whom they decide to include in their study.

Collecting data: How old are we?

First let's start with yourselves. What do you think is the youngest age of someone who might be in a [first grade] class? What would the oldest probably be?

Use the students' suggestions to write a list of possible ages on the board, for example:

    5
    6
    7
    8

How could we show how many children in our class are these different ages?

Try to get several different ideas about how students could show the ages of everyone in the class. Students' imaginations may be sparked if you point out the available tools: the chalkboard, squared paper, stick-on notes, interlocking cubes, other things to count with. If a child simply says, "Count" or "Make checks," ask for more details:

How would you count? How would we know where to put the checks?

Student suggestions might include the following:

▼ All the 5-year-olds raise their hands, then the 6-year-olds, and so forth. Count them and write the number down.

▼ Each student goes up to the board and makes a check by his or her age.

▼ Each student takes a stick-on note and puts it next to the right age.

▼ All the 5-year-olds stand together; all the 6-year-olds stand together, and so forth. Each group counts how many they have and writes their count next to the age on the board.

▼ Each student makes a tower of interlocking cubes showing his or her age—one cube for each year—then all the towers are lined up in a single display.

Try two or three of your students' suggestions so that you end up with two or three different methods and two or three different displays of results.

If no one in the group has suggested tallying, this is a good opportunity to show students

how they can use tallies. For kindergarten, you may want to keep the count by ones; for first graders, you may want to show your students how to group by fives:

5 |||
6 卌 |||
7 卌 卌 ||
8 |||

Describing the data: How old is our class?

After all the displays are completed, ask students what information they can get from looking at them. Students will certainly notice how many children there are at each age level, but encourage them to say as much as they can about what these numbers show and to use comparison words such as *more, less, a lot less, just two more, about twice as many,* and so forth. Students may also realize that the graph shows how many students are in the class.

What could a visitor to our room—say, somebody's mother—tell from this graph? What would she know about our ages? What else could she tell? Are there things about our ages she couldn't tell from this graph? Which graph do you think does the best job of showing our ages? Why?

The purpose of this part of the discussion is not necessarily to choose one "right" graph.

All of the representations show some information; each may have its strengths and disadvantages. Students may also have personal preferences about which graphs they can use most easily.

What would happen if we did graphs of our ages again next month? Would they be just the same? Would anything change?

Have students consider what the graph might look like in one month, two months, at the end of the school year, or a year from now. Let them discuss their theories about what changes there would be. Students may want to use the birthday chart you made in the first investigation as they think about these issues.

Introducing a new problem: The ages of people in our families

Now you've collected all your ages; next you're going to be getting information about the ages of people in your families. Does anyone have a younger brother or sister? What age? What about an older brother or sister? What is the youngest age we might find? What's the oldest we might find? Who knows how old one of their parents is? About how old do you think most mothers are?

Students contribute some examples and speculate a bit about the information they will be gathering. Discuss with the students whose ages they will collect. Students often want to include ages of all siblings and

parents, even if they do not all live in the same place. Some want to include pets. Others with close extended families may want to include grandparents, cousins, aunts, and uncles. If any students live with other adult guardians—uncles, grandparents, foster parents, and so forth—make sure to include them in the discussion. There is really no reason why students need to limit the data they collect, but you will want to make sure that everyone has at least the ages of siblings and important adults in their families for the activities in Sessions 2 through 5.

Hand out copies of Student Sheet 1, *Record of family ages,* and—if you wish—the letter to parents (page 63). Allow students enough time to collect the information on ages of people in their families before Session 2.

☞ Keep the age charts constructed in this session and refer to them periodically during the rest of the school year: Have the counts changed? How have they changed? Why have they changed?

Extension: Using graphing software

If you have access to a computer and a simple piece of graphing software, students can enter their age information into the computer to make a bar graph.

A simple software graphing tool for young children, the *Dynamic Bargrapher,* is available for a limited time from TERC. This tool is written in Logo, and you must have LCSI Logo II in order to run the program. Contact Alana Parkes, TERC, 2067 Massachusetts Avenue, Cambridge, MA 02140 for information about availability and price. ■

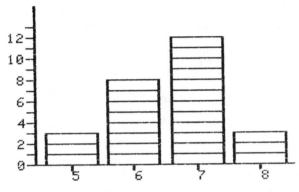

AGES IN OUR CLASS
Graph made with *DYNAMIC BARGRAPHER*

SESSION 2 AND 3 ACTIVITIES

Representing the data: Family portraits and hundred boards

Working in small groups, students represent their family data in two ways. First, they make a picture that includes everyone in their families (including themselves) and label each person with her or his age (and name, also, if they wish). Second, using individual hundred boards (page 67 or 69), each student circles or marks in some way the ages of all family members.

This work might be broken into two separate small-group sessions—one for pictures, one for hundred boards. As students make their pictures, they informally compare ages, using the terms *older, younger,* and *the same.* During the work with hundred boards, you can facilitate a great deal of talk about number relationships if you meet with each small group while it is working. The task of finding numbers on the hundred board will be quite different for different students, and you will be able to learn a great deal by observing and interacting with students as they work with the boards. Some students will already be familiar with the organization of the hundred board and will be able to find any number quickly, while others will look for each number randomly. Some students will count from the beginning every time. Others will be able to figure out how much

older one person is than another by counting on the board.

Playing with the data: How much are all your ages together?

When the hundred boards are completed, meet with each small group to discuss the ages they have on the boards:

Who is the oldest family member? Who is the youngest? How many brothers and sisters are there?

Then ask each student in the small group to make a tower of interlocking cubes to show his or her age.

So we have a 6, and a 6, and a 6, and a 6, and a 5, and a 5. If we put Felice's tower together with Alexei's, how many cubes would we have?

Students speculate about what number it would be, then put the two towers together and count them. Instead of putting the towers together, another approach is to take the two towers apart and put the cubes, one at a time, onto a hundred board, starting at one, so that students can see what numeral the cubes end up on. Try a couple more combinations of students' age towers. Usually students will suggest adding *all* the towers of their own ages together to see how many cubes that would be. Students will probably spontaneously compare the total of their ages to the individual ages on their boards. Are any of their parents the same age as the total of their ages? For a sample discussion, see the Dialogue Box, *Adding our ages together* (following).

☞ This activity, invented by a group of kindergarteners, seems to lend itself to a playfulness with numbers that we would like to encourage. The kindergarten students were not bothered by whether their addition represented anything "real" or not, so we decided not to be concerned, either. ∎

❝❞DIALOGUE BOX
Adding our ages together

What if we put Kyle's tower together with Alexei's tower? Who can figure out how many we might have?

KYLE: I know, 6 and 6 is 12.

How do you know?

KYLE: I just know it.

Kyle thinks it's 12. Who has some way to figure it out?

FELICE: We could put them together and count.

OK. We will. First, any other ideas how much it will be?

FERNANDO: 12. It's 12.

How do you know?

FERNANDO: I looked at each block with my eyes and I went by twos, 7, **8**, 9, **10**, 11, **12**.

MATT: It's going to be as much as my sister.

[*Later, after trying other combinations, including 5 and 5; 6 and 5; 6 and 6 and 6*] . . .

LYNNE: Let's put them all.

FERNANDO: Yeah, all of them in a big tower.

What do you think will happen if we add [*points at each Unifix cube tower in turn*] **6 plus 6 plus 6 plus 6 plus 5 plus 5?**

MATT: It'll be up to here.

ALEXEI: It will be about 20.

KYLE: Maybe it will be as much as one of our parents.

Do you think it could be as much as one of your parents? What do you all think? How big do you think this is going to be?

LYNNE: It's going to be bigger than 20.

FELICE: Let's add more and make it up to 35—that's my dad's age.

Do you think this might be up to 35?

FELICE: Maybe about 35 or 25.

Any other ideas?

FERNANDO: I don't think it'll be up to my mom.

OK, let's count and see.

[*Later*] . . .

EVERYONE: . . . 31, 32, 33, 34!

MATT: It's my mom's age.

FELICE: One more cube and it's my dad.

Let's look on your hundred board. Where's your dad?

FELICE: See, . . . 34, 35, that's my dad.

Anyone else have someone close to 34? ∎

SESSION 4 ACTIVITIES

Organizing the data: Us and our sisters and brothers

Make sure students have their completed *Record of family ages* (Student Sheet 1) or family portraits for reference during this session. Also plan to look back at the charts you made in Session 1, showing the ages of students in the class.

Today we're going to make a chart to show your ages and the ages of all your brothers and sisters.

Make a tally or chart of the ages of members of the class and their siblings (*siblings* is a word students enjoy learning). To maximize personal involvement in this chart, students can write each sibling's name and age on an index card or stick-on note. Students make cards for themselves as well. Use one color for members of the class, another for sisters, another for brothers. (If you do not have different-colored cards or notes, you might pre-cut different shapes—a square for class members, circles for sisters, triangles for brothers—or the class can choose three simple symbols that students can draw on their cards.) As students complete their cards, they bring them up and attach them to the chart next to the corresponding age.

If some students have baby sisters or brothers who are not yet 1 year old, you will have the opportunity for an interesting

discussion about where to put these children on your chart. Some students may want to call them "0 years old" while others may argue for "between 0 and 1." Let as many students as possible have something to say about this before coming to some decision.

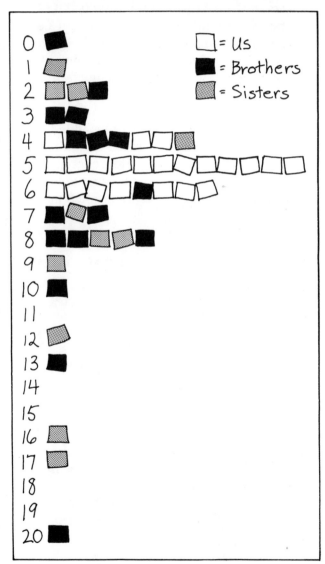

Describing the data: What can we see from the chart?

Encourage students to talk about what they can see on the chart:

"There are a lot of 8s . . . The yellow stickers are all around the same place . . . My baby brother is the youngest . . . Fives is the most . . . Nobody has a 14 or a 15 . . ."

Talk with students about why cards for brothers and sisters are scattered while their own cards are in a cluster. If there are any siblings in the same age cluster as the class members, students are often interested in why someone the same age is not in their class. Where else could they be?

Extensions

▼ Use the chart to generate problems about number relationships. For example: Sumi's brother is 2; how long will it be until he is the age Sumi is now? How much older is Melissa's brother than she is? Students work in pairs with counters, cubes, hundred boards, or the chart itself to create and figure out problems such as these.

▼ Make a similar chart of pet ages, with different symbols or colors representing different kinds of pets (cats, dogs, gerbils, and so forth). ■

SESSION 5 ACTIVITIES

Introducing the problem: Who is oldest?

Begin the discussion by referring back to the chart the class made in Session 4 and to any comments the students made about the youngest siblings.

In the last session, when we made a chart of you and all your siblings, you said that Rosalie's sister and Gustave's brother were the youngest. Gustave and Rosalie were going to find out their exact birthdays, so we could see which one was the very youngest. So now we know about the youngest people in our families. What about the oldest? How could we find out who the oldest people are?

Encourage students to make comments about the oldest in their own families ("I bet my aunt is the oldest; she's 61") and to think of ways to find out who is the oldest in all the data they have collected ("We could list all the parents and the grandparents on the board and then look and see which is the oldest," "We could make a chart like the one we did for sisters and brothers," "Each person could say their oldest and we could see which is highest"). Tell students that you will come back to their ideas about how to show the oldest people after they have worked on the problem in small groups.

☛ If only a few students have grandparent data, you may want to have everyone consider only parents and guardians first so that the students with grandparent data are not looked at as having an "unfair" advantage in having the oldest person in their data. Because the ages are generally lower, parent/guardian data are also more manageable as students make cube or paper towers in the next part of the activity. Of course, some students' guardians might *be* grandparents, and you do not want to leave them out, so you will have to make the decisions about which family members to include in this part of the investigation according to what best fits your students and their data. Grandparents might be added at the end to the whole class representation of the oldest people to see how they change the data; or, an additional activity using only grandparent data could be undertaken (see the Extension, page 61).

Organizing the data: Looking at the oldest in our families

To be sure that students are engaged in looking at the data and thinking about these higher numbers, have them explore this question in small groups first. If possible, meet with each small group.

In the small groups, each student builds a tower of interlocking cubes to show the age of the oldest member of his or her family. Since some of these towers will be long and unwieldy, students will need table or floor space on which to lay their work, both as they build them and when comparing them.

Students can work together in pairs to build the towers (e.g., Cal helps Barbara build the tower of 32 cubes for her mother and Barbara helps Cal build the 35 tower for his mother), since counting and recounting these higher numbers is difficult. Encourage students to invent strategies for counting and keeping track of their counts, such as putting in a different colored cube at 10, 20, and 30, or making each group of 5 a different color.

Within each small group, students label their towers using an index card or stick-on note, and compare them by laying them next to each other. Support the conversation that is likely to happen spontaneously around this comparison since students are very interested in *biggest, oldest,* and other extremes at this age level. However, you can also pose questions to extend this discussion:

How many of these are in the 30s? the 40s? What numbers do we skip when we go from Sumi's dad to Karen's? Are any of these towers twice as big as another one? The tower for Jesse's grandmother is so tall; how could we make it easier to count? How many years would we have to add on to David's mom for her to be as old as Karima's aunt?

Organizing the data: Who has the oldest family member?

There are many ways of organizing the class data. Since at this point in the unit, students have a great deal of experience with different kinds of representations, involve them as much as possible in deciding how to show everyone's "oldest person." Possibilities include the following:

▼ Line up all the interlocking cube towers in order of height; keep the students' labels with their towers so that each student can still recognize his or her individual tower.

▼ Each student cuts and tapes a "tower" out of squared paper (page 71) to show the age of the oldest person in his or her data; these towers are posted on a bulletin board or chalkboard.

▼ Students write the name and age of their oldest people on an index card or stick-on note; these are posted on a number line.

▼ Each student circles the age of his or her oldest person on a large hundred chart.

You might choose to do more than one of these (perhaps one "tower" representation and one more graph-like representation) so that students can see the data represented in different ways. The "tower" representations show clearly the size of each piece of data and how it compares in amount to every other "tower." The number line and hundred board representations show only the *values* of the data and emphasize where each piece of data falls in the series of counting numbers. Thus, the X on the number line for the

student whose age is 6 looks exactly the same as the X for her sister who is 12. It is the *placement* of these X's, rather than their appearance, that shows the difference in age. These two kinds of representations—one in which the size of each piece of data is preserved, and one in which the data are summarized by numeric values—are really quite different. Students will continue to expand their understanding of the meaning of the counting numbers if they can view such different representations side by side.

Extension

Some students may want to collect new data; for example, they may now want to know ages of grandparents who were not included in the initial data collection. Perhaps some students have living great-grandparents who could be included in the data. A chart for grandparents' ages might be made if students are still interested in who is oldest. ∎

SESSION 6 ACTIVITIES (Optional)

Putting it all together: The ages of everyone in our families

Some first grade classes have enjoyed making a giant graph of all the ages of people in their families. You will need to prepare a large number line, going from 0 up to the oldest age in the students' data, with enough room between numbers to put on stick-on notes or stick-on dots or to color in squares. Three pieces of chart paper fastened together with the long side on the bottom will probably be big enough. Some teachers have used one of the commercial 1-100 number lines for the base of this graph.

To make the graph, students choose different colors for each category of data they want to show: sisters, brothers, mothers, fathers, grandparents, and so forth. They decide on categories as a group: Do they want one color for parents, or do they want to split up parents into mothers and fathers; or, if some students live with adults other than parents, do they want to have one color for the male adults in the house, one for female adults?

Keep in mind that families and who is part of them constitute a sensitive issue for many students and that, for first graders, their personal data is vitally important. One first grader was terribly concerned that her two aunts, with whom she lived, be included, and that they have a special color to show they were aunts. In the overall discussion of categories, a balance must be struck between recognizing students' personal needs and creating a manageable chart with a manageable number of colors, as in the following discussion:

Mark wants to put in Sheila, because she's an adult who lives in his house, and she's like part of the family, but she isn't a mother or aunt, so should we use yellow, like for mothers?

PAUL: That wouldn't be right, because we'd look at that and think it's one of the mothers.

Who has a solution?

LILUE: Make a different-colored one.

That's one solution. Who can think of something else we could do?

ALEXEI: We could just say that all the adults who are women are yellow.

SIMON: No, we should be able to tell who the mothers are.

JANE: We could like put a dot or something of a different color or something on the yellow.

What do you think, Mark? What would you like to do?

MARK: I like the dot idea, because I'm going to put up a yellow for my mom, and then I could put a dot on the one for Sheila so that's a little different.

After students decide on categories and colors, you will need to orchestrate the creation of the chart. You may want students to post the data for one category at a time; if so, hand out stick-on notes of the appropriate color for that category and have all students with someone in that category write the name and age of that person *and their own initials* on the note and place it on the chart.

Since mistakes are bound to be made and stick-on notes are bound to fall off the chart, the more information recorded on the note the better, so that the notes can be identified, replaced, or changed later. Stick-on notes are not as permanent as stick-on dots or coloring in a square above the number, but changes can be made more easily with the notes. Once everyone feels confident that all the information is in the right place on the chart, you might tape them onto the chart more securely, or replace the stick-on notes with stick-on dots.

When the chart is completed, leave it in a prominent place. Much of the discussion about the chart will take place informally if students are given a chance to view it and talk about it with each other. You can also have a discussion with the whole group, asking them about the differences they see:

Why are all the blues down at one end? Which color stretches the farthest? Why is that? Why do some greens (siblings) reach up to where the yellows (mothers) begin? (Or, if they don't, why not?) If you made this graph again at the end of the year (or next fall), what could change? If you asked the other first grade for the ages of their families, do you think the chart would look the same? What if you asked the fifth graders? ■

Dear Parents:

Your child's class is collecting information about ages. The children have already talked about their own ages. Now they are ready to collect information about their families.

Please help your child fill out the attached sheet, identifying each family member by family role or name and age. For example, completed sentences might read like this:

> My mother is 30 years old.

> My sister Tara is 9 years old.

Children can include anyone they feel is a family member. Usually, they will want to include mother, father, and guardians, as well as brothers and sisters, even if they do not all live at the same address. They may also want to include other people who live with them—a grandmother, cousin, stepbrother, or even a pet!

It is fine to help with spelling and to show your child how to write the numbers. You might write the words on a separate piece of paper for your child to copy. You can even help with the actual writing if the task becomes too long.

The children are looking forward to putting together all this information about ages. These numbers will provide a meaningful context in which they can continue to learn more about numbers and what they represent.

Thanks for your help.

_____ is _____ years old.

_____ is _____ years old.

_____ is _____ years old.

_____ is _____ years old.

_____ is _____ years old.

_____ is _____ years old.

_____ is _____ years old.

_____ is _____ years old.

0	1	2	3	4	5	6	7	8	9
10	11	12	13	14	15	16	17	18	19
20	21	22	23	24	25	26	27	28	29
30	31	32	33	34	35	36	37	38	39
40	41	42	43	44	45	46	47	48	49
50	51	52	53	54	55	56	57	58	59
60	61	62	63	64	65	66	67	68	69
70	71	72	73	74	75	76	77	78	79
80	81	82	83	84	85	86	87	88	89
90	91	92	93	94	95	96	97	98	99

1	2	3	4	5	6	7	8	9	10
11	12	13	14	15	16	17	18	19	20
21	22	23	24	25	26	27	28	29	30
31	32	33	34	35	36	37	38	39	40
41	42	43	44	45	46	47	48	49	50
51	52	53	54	55	56	57	58	59	60
61	62	63	64	65	66	67	68	69	70
71	72	73	74	75	76	77	78	79	80
81	82	83	84	85	86	87	88	89	90
91	92	93	94	95	96	97	98	99	100